A
Harlequin
Romance

OTHER
Harlequin Romances
by MARGERY HILTON

Many of these titles are available at your local bookseller,
or through the Harlequin Reader Service.

For a free catalogue listing all available Harlequin Romances,
send your name and address to:

HARLEQUIN READER SERVICE,
M.P.O. Box 707, Niagara Falls, N.Y. 14302
Canadian address: Stratford, Ontario, Canada.

or use order coupon at back of book.

MIRANDA'S MARRIAGE

by

MARGERY HILTON

HARLEQUIN BOOKS   TORONTO
WINNIPEG

Original hard cover edition published in 1973
by Mills & Boon Limited.

© Margery Hilton 1973

SBN 373-01752-9

Harlequin edition published January 1974

Printed in Canada

1752

CHAPTER ONE

FOR the second time in the space of twenty minutes the door of number three Byrne Square slammed violently, shattering the peace of the dignified, tree-lined square.

The door shuddered in its frame, and a little grey tabby cat suspended her face-washing activity to look up reproachfully at the tall, furious man descending the six steps to the pavement. Well tailored grey Dacron brushed her soft fur, and well-shod feet flashed past her small white paws, narrowly missing one of them. Seconds later a third slam, metallic this time, echoed through the air. The wine-red Mercedes pulled away from the kerb, and the little cat blinked, then placidly resumed her toilet; strange how easily human beings lost their tempers.

Jason Steele wove into the traffic stream and considered that he had every reason to lose his temper. He'd been made to look an all-time fool. He'd wasted time, he'd lost the few shreds remaining to him of trust in human nature, and he'd been too blind and besotted and idiotic to see it – to say nothing of what he'd spent on the bitch. Worst of all, he'd been used.

Women!

Jason narrowly missed the red Scimitar that shot out of a concealed turning and swore under his breath. He was through with woman. Women with hearts of steel and grasping little minds hidden by innocent faces and soft yielding bodies. About as soft and innocent as a rattlesnake. Never again! He'd said it before, but this time he meant it. Twice in his life he'd been fooled by a woman. This time he'd got the message.

Three sets of traffic lights in succession baulked him, and at the third frustrating hold-up he groaned aloud. God! He wanted a drink, and the honest-to-God company of men. At least you knew where you were with a man – and with a man you could hit back . . . His grip tightened on the wheel until his knuckles gleamed white. He could strangle Mike Frears; his own second in command, a man he'd trusted. And all this time he and Catrina . . .

After a couple of stiff drinks Jason felt calmer but no less acid of temper. He came out into the night, glanced up at the clouded sky and then at his watch to find that it was still not

5

long after eight, and on a sudden impulse he decided to drive round by the office and pick up his notes on the new collateral agreement with Strangco.

His evening was ruined anyway; none of his cronies had been in the Gresham tonight and his appetite had deserted him. He might as well salvage something of the night, and he had enough work waiting him in all conscience. Squiring the Catrinas of this world was a demanding business, and he'd paid too much heed to her demands these last few weeks and too little to the mounting pressures of the pile on his desk.

The head office of Carona-Steele were housed in a glass and concrete tower of some twenty-four storeys overlooking the Thames near Blackfriars. A dim light in the reception foyer and an isolated gleam high up the dark side hinted that the building was not quite so deserted as it seemed when Jason parked the car and strode across the forecourt.

The last of the cleaners was just leaving. She gave him a curious look as she passed him, turning up a tired, work-worn face which nevertheless registered instant recognition. Jason ignored the look and spoke briefly to the night guard who had appeared from a small side door. The big Alsatian dog at the man's side also stared at the tall man striding across to the lift, the slight lift of his sagacious head also betraying curiosity and no trace of awe because Jason Steele at thirty-seven headed the British division of a multi-million international combine and was reputed to be as ruthless as he was brilliant.

The lift doors opened silently and Jason stepped through, to be borne up to his suite on the twenty-first floor. He stepped out on to carpet thick enough to deaden the heaviest of footsteps, then halted abruptly, instantly aware of two things. First, a warning instinct told him all was not as it should be; secondly, that the isolated light he had noticed from below was coming from his own suite.

He frowned. It was known he was in the building – the master and pilot switches would not be in operation, but there certainly should not be any light within his inner office. It was little over a couple of hours since he'd left it, and he'd certainly not been guilty of leaving any lights on.

His mouth grim, Jason did not flick down the switch near the lift entrance. He walked silently across the dim reception room, the white chink under the far door seeming to grow brighter as his eyes became attuned to the dimness, and after the briefest of pauses threw open the door.

At his first swift glance the spacious office appeared empty. But the audible gasp proved this appearance to be false.

Jason advanced, his hand reaching out for the alarm bell. 'Come out,' he said grimly. 'I know you're—'

Sheer surprise clipped his demand and stayed his finger over the bell. He stared at the head rising above the back of the deep white leather armchair and gasped.

Two wide terrified eyes stared back at him, and two small hands clutched the back of the chair so tightly they made deep indentations in the leather. The girl's mouth rounded, a further expression of horror, and trembled, as though trying to utter some response, but all that came was a second gasp, small and choked and inarticulate.

Jason recovered first. Three peremptory strides took him as far as the chair. The girl shrank back from his anger and tried to evade his grasp. She was half kneeling, half crouched in the depths of the chair, and he caught her arm, yanking her ungently to her feet.

'Who the devil are you?'

The girl's soft lips parted. She seemed frozen with shock. Jason's grip tightened. He shook her without realizing what he was doing as he demanded: 'What the hell are you doing in here?'

'I – I—' She licked dry lips. 'Don't you know me, Mr. Steele?' she quavered. 'I work here.'

'Not in here, you don't.' His grip slackened, but his stare was icy. 'There are some five hundred employees in this section, maybe more,' he said sardonically. 'I've never had the time to make the acquaintance of all of them.'

She rubbed at the marks already welling on her arm where his fingers had bitten into the delicate skin. 'I realize that,' she said unsteadily, 'I'm sorry if I startled you, Mr. Steele.'

He saw the small convulsive movement in her throat as she swallowed, but his gaze did not soften. He went to the drinks cabinet and took out a glass. As he splashed soda into the bourbon he said grimly: 'Well, I'm waiting for your explanation, Miss – Miss whatever your name is.'

There was a pause. Jason raised the glass to his lips and watched her over the rim. Several suspicions, none of them particularly pleasant, occurred to him, and he frowned.

7

'Making it up?' he accused. 'Or would you prefer to wait for the police?'

'Oh no!' she gasped, and took a step forward. 'It's Meake,' she said in a resigned voice. 'Miranda Rose Meake.'

'Miranda Rose Meake!' Glass in hand, he almost choked. 'Oh, come off it, darling! You've got to be making it up.'

'It's true! It *is* my name,' she protested.

Jason's mouth curved sardonically. Yes, it must be. For who, outside the entertainment profession, would concoct a name like that? Miranda Rose Meake . . . If only parents realized . . . he checked his speculation, his glance turning from her to register various other oddities that defiled the aesthetic taste of his luxuriously furnished burgundy and white office. A suede shoulder bag lay on the floor beside the burgundy and white hide settee, an open shopping bag lay against the arm, spilling, among other things, a dark blue scarf and a – yes, a small and decidedly intimate article of feminine underwear.

Jason expelled a heavy breath and passed on with disfavour to the array on his otherwise immaculate desk. A paper package that appeared to hold sandwiches and a half eaten pie, an opened carton of milk, a bar of chocolate, a torch, and a paperback edition of one of Iris Murdoch's novels.

The pressure of anger swelled in his chest. He returned a chill glance to her. 'I'm waiting for an explanation, Miss Meake.'

She took a quivering breath. 'It – it's difficult to explain.'

'These things usually are.'

Her thin shoulders seemed to brace themselves defensively. 'I know it – all this,' she gave a despairing little gesture, 'must look awful, and you must have got—' Suddenly she saw the betraying bag and bent feverishly over the settee, scooping things off the white cushion and back into the bag. She straightened. 'I'm terribly sorry if you got a shock when you walked in and found – it must have—' She seemed to have difficulty in going on and turned away from his dark, accusing stare.

He said cruelly, 'Tears will cut no ice with me. Now listen, I intend to have an explanation of this unwarranted intrusion before I give myself the pleasure of firing you personally and throwing you out of the building, along with all the junk you had the effrontery to bring in with you.' His voice rose. 'The explanation's beginning to look pretty obvious. Who else were you planning to smuggle in? A nice little party. Or your personal hippy commune? Pity I had to come back and spoil your little game. Or is there a more sinister motive involved?' His eyes darkened. 'Perhaps I got here just in time. I can see I shall have to inquire into the security measures here before—'

His flow of tirade checked. She was no longer making any attempt to hide the trembling of her shoulders and the tears spilling down her cheeks. Her mouth worked tremulously, choking her words as she whispered: 'I'm sorry, Mr. Steele. It was unpardonable, I know. If only I could make you understand, but—'

She shook her head, starting to gather up the pathetic little packages of sandwiches and chocolate. She stuffed them blindly into the bag and looked helplessly at the carton of milk. She picked it up, then set it down again, giving the same little despairing shake of her head, and snatched at a dark blue suede jacket lying on the other chair. 'I'm sorry,' she repeated. 'I – I can only say that none of your fears are true. I don't come from a hippy commune, and I didn't come to steal – you can search my things if you don't believe me – and I quite understand that you have every reason to be angry – but I'll go now and—'

'No!' He barred her way to the door.

She stopped short and looked up at him. Her long silky lashes sparkled with tears and the bruises of weeping were already painting their dark smudges under her eyes.

She said, 'Let me go, please. I can't do more than apologize.'

'Just a minute. I'm not through yet.' Almost without realizing it he had seized her arm. 'Is that all you can say?'

Imperceptibly, a change had come into her expression. 'What do you expect me to say?' she said flatly.

'You might make a slightly more convincing explanation.'

She sighed. 'Would you believe it? Even if you were prepared to listen without heaping up more accusations?'

'Why, you insolent little minx!' There was bluster in his voice, yet it sounded forced in his own ears. A new sense was troubling him, something vaguely like shame, and the unwelcome realization that he had vented the full spleen of his anger on her. But he *had* given her a chance to defend herself. Damn it! He'd asked her, hadn't he? Grudgingly, he said, 'I'm listening.'

She took a deep breath and upturned her face to meet his

9

accusing stare. She had regained a measure of control now, and although her eyes still swam with unshed tears her mouth was taut and there was an unconscious air of dignity about the poised head.

'Please let go – you're hurting my arm,' she said quietly.

In some way the balance had swayed. He had become the one ill at ease and it was a sensation both foreign and displeasing. He said ungraciously: 'I didn't intend to. But why the devil did you give me such a hell of a shock?'

'I never meant to. I've told you. If I'd known you were coming back tonight I'd have thought of something else. But I never expected . . .'

'Thought of what?' He frowned. 'An alternative to what?'

She sighed. 'I suppose I'll have to tell you, or you'll never believe me. You've fired me, anyway, so it can't make things any worse. I was going to spend the night here.'

'Here?' He was flabbergasted. 'In my office?'

She nodded.

'But what on earth for?'

'Why does a person spend the night anywhere?' she said ironically, and answered her own rhetoric: 'Because spending it on the street isn't much fun.'

His eyes betrayed his amazement. 'Have you no home?'

She smiled faintly at his incredulous expression. 'I share a flat with three other girls. I suppose one could call it home.'

'Then why aren't you there tonight?'

Her glance fell and she turned her head away. 'Can't I say a kind of – of emergency prevented me, and leave it at that?'

'Illness?'

There was no confirmatory movement of the averted head and Jason experienced a flash of unease he could not explain. He said sharply: 'Are you in trouble of some kind?'

'No – at least,' her mouth twisted wryly, 'not if you don't count this.'

Jason walked impatiently to the desk and swung round. 'Then why? Quite frankly, you're not making sense.'

'I know.' Unexpectedly, she came towards him and faced him with unconscious appeal in her direct gaze. 'But I doubt if you'd understand if I did tell you the truth. Can't you believe me, that I didn't come to steal? That all I wanted was shelter for the night?'

He did not respond instantly, and she made a despairing

little gesture that somehow encompassed herself and the luxurious fittings in the big room. It was as though she implored him to refute his suspicions, and despite himself Jason felt that odd sense of shame again. His glance flickered to the gaudy plastic shopping bag and he remembered the innocuous little collection he had glimpsed, intimate and innocent . . . He gave a brusque gesture. 'There isn't a great deal here, except office equipment. Nor have I levelled that specific accusation.'

'Not in so many words,' she said quietly, and he saw her glance travel across his desk, itemizing the silver desk lighter, a couple of rather expensive pens in an onyx holder, and the ostentatious crystal and gold cigarette box which had been Catrina's first and only gift to him. The wide gaze travelled on, back to his face.

'Can't you just accept my apology and let me go?' she asked.

'Where to?'

She betrayed surprise at the abrupt question he had asked without thinking. 'Does that matter?'

'You must have somewhere to go?'

'That's my worry, isn't it?' She hitched the suede bag strap more firmly on to her shoulder and moved towards the door.

'Just a minute.'

The sharp turn of her head betrayed the instant return of alarm. He read defensiveness in the mute compressed line of her lips, yet the slender fingers whitening as they gripped the door edge were strangely defenceless.

'What makes you so sure I wouldn't understand?' he asked. slowly.

She looked at him and her eyes were candid. 'You're too angry, and why should you care?'

Jason gave a sharp exclamation, and suspicion returned to his eyes as he stared at her. Just what did she mean by that? Was she deliberately trying to make him curious? They were all the same; as devious as a politician and as treacherous as a maelstrom. Then he saw beneath the assumed indifference to the wan weariness that could not be faked. He said: 'Don't you think you owe me the benefit of the doubt, if not an explanation?'

For a long moment she did not move. The play of emotion on her small, mobile features was rapid and easily read: the indecision, doubt, despair, and then resignation as she came to a decision. She stared steadily at a point somewhere over his shoulder as she said slowly: 'I told you; I share a flat with three other girls. I don't know if you've ever experienced living in three small rooms with three other people.'

She hesitated, and he nodded impatiently.

'There's very little privacy – none, in fact. It only works out if you're prepared to accept that, and try not to quarrel when it gets so inconvenient you want to scream.'

Again she hesitated, and he barely suppressed a fresh surge of irritation. Why couldn't she get to the point? So what? It was obvious there'd been a squalling match and her mates had pitched her out, but did she have to take it so damned seriously? His mouth curved ironically: these kids swarmed down into the city, eternally hopeful of the wonderful swinging life they were going to have, and endured conditions that would make their parents blench if they could see them.

He said, 'Yes, but these things happen all the time. You have to learn to stand on your own feet and not be too hasty. Did they throw you out or did you walk out?'

She started, and the distant gaze switched abruptly to his face. 'No – it isn't like that at all. You don't understand. It's just for this one night. It wasn't convenient for me to be there tonight.'

He began to see, and almost laughed. His imagination must be getting senile if he'd forgotten the problems of courtship in a house that wasn't your own. His mind travelled back to the time when he'd spent six months at the Paris branch. When that new kid came over, Suzanne – he'd forgotten her second name – and young Luke Byland had gone berserk over her. Jason grinned to himself at the memory. She'd really led Luke a dance, and every time he got his foot in the door the flatmate was sitting there. A beautiful blonde dragon of a flatmate. Jason had made the hastiest revision ever of his personal plans and agreed to aid the despairing Luke. To take care of the beautiful dragon for that week-end would be a pleasure. It was unfortunate that she happened to have a fiancé, and even more unfortunate that the fiancé happened to be a particularly tough Teutonic type possessed of, among other things, a black belt and a suspicious turn of mind. Jason had bowed out regretfully, leaving the despairing Luke to devise other methods of enticing the ewe lamb from under the dragon's wing.

Jason grinned again at the memory, and the girl said sharply:

'It's not funny!'

He started. He'd forgotten the invader. 'Sorry,' he murmured absently, 'I was thinking of something else.'

'You aren't even listening,' she accused, 'after making all that fuss!'

The amusement ebbed from his face. Suddenly he was bored with the subject of her petty little squabbles with her friends, whoever they were. He said curtly, 'I was listening. But what's all the fuss about? If your mate wants to entertain a man without you around surely you could have stayed with somebody for the night, or gone to a hotel, for that matter.'

'Hotels cost money,' she said bitterly, 'but you wouldn't think of that.'

He shrugged, wondering why he should bother even to make suggestions. Better get rid of her and collect those notes without wasting any more of the night. He pulled out his keys and turned to open the top drawer of the desk.

'It's the end of the month,' she said flatly. 'I'm broke. And you still don't understand.'

Jason groaned softly under his breath, his attention on the papers rustling softly under his fingers. 'Is there anything to understand, Miss Meake, except that you seem to have a marked talent for taking impertinent liberties?'

There was no reply, only a shadow passing across his desk. He looked up and saw she had crossed to the window. She stared out at the glittering carpet of London's lights stretching out to the black sky and said slowly:

'They're having a party – a certain kind of a party. They wanted me to make the number up. I said I couldn't. And that's why I'm here.'

Something in the flat tones made him frown. They were too emotionless. Despite himself he experienced that odd flash of unease again. What the devil was the matter with the girl? He stared at the tensed line of her shoulders, the stiffly poised head and the shadowed profile just discernible against the darkly reflecting glass.

'What do you mean? A certain kind of party?' he exclaimed.

He sensed rather than heard the sigh she gave, and the first conclusion to leap to his mind was that she meant drugs. But before he could utter the suspicion she said despairingly:

'You take it all for granted now, don't you? Nobody raises

an eyebrow, and anyone who doesn't want to play along is scared, or a prudish spoilsport.'

'If you mean what I think you mean – drugs – I certainly don't take it all for granted,' he said sharply. 'And if that's the kind of thing going on at your flat you want to get out of it right away. Never mind how they taunt you. Just get out – while you can.'

His words must have revealed more distaste than he realized, for she turned her head and looked over her shoulder at him. The wry little smile twisted her mouth again, then was lost in disillusion once more.

'Isn't that what I've just done? What all this fuss is about?'

His mouth compressed, but before he could frame a suitable retort that could bring this troublesome business to an end she gave a shrug and returned her gaze to the window.

'It isn't a pot party this time, Mr. Steele, just another sleep-around.'

Jason's dark brows drew together. He forgot the papers in his hand and the impulse to get rid of the girl. Something she'd said a few moments previously flashed back into his mind. *Prudish spoilsport* ... An old-fashioned epithet with a decidedly Victorian qualification in front of it. Was she? Or was it her particular line? But why decamp for his office if she ...?

'Do your friends live a little too fast for you?' he asked dryly.

'They're not my real friends,' she said in a low voice. 'They're just people who happen to have got on the same route as me at this particular time of my life.'

Her reply surprised him. There was no trace of the cynicism that would have sharpened the same remark had it come from Catrina's lips, or the soft, provocative little moue that she ... For a moment he forgot the girl, forgot the office, and remembered only Catrina's tempting mouth, the way it invited, evaded, whispered in the moment before it promised, yielded, excited ... *Oh, to hell with her!* He was well out of it. With an effort he dragged his mind away from the fantasies memory would weave and made his gaze deliberate over the slender form of the girl by the window.

'Are you a prudish spoilsport, Miss Meake?' he said with rather more derision in his tone than he had intended.

The hazel silky head moved abruptly. There was a hesitation, then she said quietly: 'I don't think it matters much to you what I am. I should think all this time being wasted is of more concern.' Suddenly she swung round. 'Not mine – yours.'

She stood there, silent, a mingling of concern and inquiry on her face, as though she awaited his permission to make her escape. He hesitated, and the apprehension fluttered again in her wide, serious eyes. 'I – I can't stay here now,' she said awkwardly, making a small, appealing gesture, 'so if you . . .' She let the gesture finish for her, and he sensed more strongly the return of her fear.

Suddenly he had a desire to be out of the building. He glanced at his watch, saw that it was nearly nine and knew surprise. Hours, not a mere twenty minutes or so, seemed to have elapsed since the moment he walked into this room . . . He stuffed the papers into his briefcase and looked up to see that the girl had not moved. She stayed motionless, still watching him with that wide, apprehensive gaze, and abruptly he closed the case.

'Come and have something to eat,' he said.

'What?'

She stared, and Jason felt surprise. He had made the suggestion without thinking. Conversely, her exclamation of surprise piqued him. Girls were not in the habit of querying his invitations to eat out; if they did, they tended to eat first and argue afterwards, he thought sardonically. Women were all the same, out for what they could get out of a man, then they screamed if he took them at their own valuation.

'I said come and have something to eat,' he repeated.

'With you?' She looked as though she didn't believe him.

'And why not? Do I have something repulsive growing out of my ears?' he demanded.

'No, but . . .' she shook her head helplessly. 'I thought . . .'

'Oh, for heaven's sake stop arguing.' He picked up the case, switched off the desk light, and moved towards the door. 'I won't eat you.'

'Yes, I know, but . . .' still she hung back, 'I don't under-stand.'

'You don't have to.' He held the door open. 'I'm hungry, and I don't feel inclined to eat alone.'

She came forward uncertainly, and stopped. 'I shouldn't have thought you'd have wanted to eat with me.'

Jason sighed, and suppressed a desire to shake her. 'Listen, young woman, I don't think you're in a position to think. Either you do as I say, or I'll call the guard to throw you out. Which is it to be?'

She looked at him, and her mouth compressed. 'You don't leave me much choice. Very well, but I'm not exactly dressed to hit the kind of high spots I imagine you frequent.'

'I'm not hitting any of those tonight,' he told her dourly. 'We're going to a small quiet pub where the grub's good and the small talk nil.'

'Oh.' She picked up her bag and came doubtfully towards him. 'Is there such a thing as a quiet pub?'

'It's the company, not the building, that makes the noise.' He saw her out and glanced round the office before he switched off the light and closed the door.

She kept apart from him, looking fixedly at the illuminated panel while the lift sank swiftly and silently down to its cushioned halt on the ground floor. The night guard glanced at him, then at this companion, and Jason knew there was speculation behind the softly spoken 'Good night, sir,' and touch of the cap as the man glanced at his companion.

She eyed the watchful dog and as soon as they were out of earshot remarked uncertainly, 'What a magnificent animal.'

Jason muttered a response, then some inner devilment prompted him to add dryly, 'You wouldn't have thought so if you'd run into him during the night.'

'No, I suppose not.' She did not look at him.

He unlocked the car, and once again he was aware of that same tense withdrawal as in the lift. His mouth went down at the corners with ironic amusement as he swung the car in a big U-turn; what was going on in that enigmatic head of hers? Was she really as petrified as she appeared? Or was it just another act? Surely he hadn't been as grim as all that. Damn it; he'd been justified. At least she was keeping quiet, he approved grudgingly. He loathed being nattered at while driving, and most women of his acquaintance appeared to think it incumbent on them to make amusing chatter the moment he got behind the wheel.

He headed south-west, and was half-way to his favourite haunt when he made his second sudden and uncharacteristic decision that evening. At the next intersection he turned right, skirted Green Park and wove through a devious net of secondary roads towards the bacchanalian lights of Soho. A shower had fallen recently and the neons cast their liquid colours across the dark pool of the road, lending a spurious beauty to the night. A taxi disgorged a load of tourists a little way ahead, and the street touts for the strip joints lurked in readiness to accost them. When Jason pulled into a parking place and stopped the girl gave him a questioning glance.

However, she did not break her silence as she got out of the car, but for the first time she drew a little closer to him as he approached a dark, cavernous doorway. The doorman greeted him by name, slid open a black and gold grille to one side of the small lobby, and the warm smoky atmosphere curled up from below. Again the girl looked at him as he motioned her down the black well with its narrow copper spiral staircase. A slowly turning mobile cast strange red patterns and whirling stripes across their faces, and Jason suppressed a grin; he'd forgotten Charlie's new face-lift; it was a little reminiscent of a descent into a black and red inferno, presided over by Charlie himself, of the dark and saturnine countenance.

'Good to see you again, sir.' Charlie materialized out of the deep red gloom and betrayed not a flicker of notice of Jason's change of feminine company. 'Your usual table? Or would the lady prefer the Rotunda?'

'The Rotunda,' Jason responded. He knew by her expression as she looked around her that she was treading fresh ground, and he wondered what would be her reaction to the huge copper table in the all black circular room around which the really off-beat young fringe of theatre-land liked to gather. It was early yet, but there were several minor notabilities and a few less minor among the diners. The black velvet wall hangings provided a perfect foil for colourful clothes, the more bizarre especially.

When they were seated Miranda turned reproachful eyes to him. 'You said a quiet pub.'

'I changed my mind.' He felt more good-humoured now and tried his smile on her. But she did not respond.

'I'm not dressed for a way-out place like this.'

'Nonsense. You can wear anything here – except a little black dress.'

'Perhaps, but I wish I wasn't in workday clothes, all the same,' she said unhappily.

'Nonsense,' he repeated, and let his gaze rove over her. 'You

17

look fine. Anyway, from the day-to-day glimpses I have of the female staff I can't say that I see much difference in the choice of some of them of working apparel and the togs they doll-up in elsewhere. There's one young woman in Accounts who usually looks as though she's ready to take off for the Ritz,' he observed.

'Oh,' recognition quickened Miranda's tone, 'that'll be Miss Harvey. She has super dress taste. But she's assistant to the chief accountant, so I suppose she can please herself.'

'And the chief accountant,' Jason said absently as the appropriate pigeonhole in his memory bank gave up its last heard item of gossip. So that was old Trayer's new bird of paradise. How long before his wife got wind of it? Jason glanced sharply at his companion, wondering if her remark carried extra meaning, but her gaze was quite innocent of guile and he added: 'Anyway, I'm still in workaday garb.'

'You're different.'

'How?' He felt amusement, and could not resist the eternal temptation to prompt feminine confidences. 'Why should I be different from countless other city businessmen?'

'Do you really have to be told?'

The quiet voice and the honesty in the serious eyes made him a little ashamed of the conceited desire for feminine admiration. 'Being the man at the top has its drawbacks, you know,' he said flatly. 'One of them is having to carry the can when something goes wrong – and the shareholders have no mercy.'

'You can go anywhere in the world. If you hail a taxi it stops,' she said. 'The waiter always sees you the moment you walk into a restaurant. If you give an order you don't need to wait to see if it's carried out – it always is. Because you have that air of authority people instinctively obey. It's a gift, I think, and it makes the difference between being a success in life or a non-success. That's how you're different,' she finished.

'Good heavens'!' said Jason, after a moment of astonishment. 'Where did you get all that? You don't even know me.'

'It isn't necessary to know a person to recognize their ability.'

'So it seems.' Jason stroked his chin and looked unseeingly at the perfectly done tournedos with its garnish of button mushrooms that the waiter was placing before him. This one appeared to have unsuspected depths. Or was it a bit of good old-fashioned blarney after his threats earlier on? Was she really in

18

full flight from a love-in, or whatever they called an orgy these days?

As she gave her attention to her fricassée he studied her unobtrusively, trying to guess at her background. She'd had a reasonable education, he'd say. Mentally she was alert enough and her voice was attractively modulated. She wasn't very old, eighteen or thereabouts; her body had the slenderness of immaturity and her mouth that way of tensing which spoke of lack of self-assurance. One front tooth wasn't quite straight, her hair was soft and free of lacquer, her brows unplucked, and her chin rather pointed. Her eyes were her best feature, he thought dispassionately. They were wide and very clear, with rich dark blue irises flecked with grey and black. Their gaze could be disconcertingly direct, and, to Jason's experienced eye, transparently innocent. Yes, she'd been perfectly truthful. This one would flee like a frightened doe from a word out of place, never mind a hand . . .

Jason checked his idle speculation. She was unlikely to cross his path again after tonight, but at least she'd supplied a diversion when he most needed one. Any company other than his own was welcome tonight.

Automatically he assumed the façade of charm which had become second nature to him when he entertained the feminine sex. It rarely failed him, and it seemed that Miss Miranda Meake was to be no exception. She appeared to be losing her fear of him, and responded more readily, if still rather shyly, to his prompting questions. Gradually a picture began to emerge and build up of her background. He was not really surprised to discover that she was an orphan and had been reared from the age of two by an elderly aunt, nor did it take him long to discover that maiden Aunt Hester's upbringing had been somewhat strict if kindly, and decidedly puritan.

Prudish, in fact, he concluded to himself with some amusement, and said carelessly: 'I bet she took some talking into letting you stretch your wings. Guardian dragons can be tougher than parents.'

'Aunt Hester wasn't a dragon,' she said in a rather constrained voice, and looked down at her plate.

Instantly Jason was attuned to the note of awkwardness. 'Wasn't?' he said softly.

'She died four months ago.'

He looked at the downbent head. 'I'm sorry.'

For a moment she was silent, and he began to fear tears, and then she gave a small shake of her head and to his surprise said abruptly: 'I seem to have talked an awful lot about myself – too much.'

'Not at all,' he said politely, hiding surprise. Few of his feminine acquaintances ever talked of anything other than themselves and their more or less frivolous desires. 'Tell me,' he prompted idly with his usual perception, 'how did it feel to have freedom thrust on you so suddenly, after such a quiet up-bringing? He leaned back, smiling a little, and she responded instantly to the warm note of invitation in his voice, exactly as he had known she would.

'It was a bit frightening at first,' she admitted slowly, 'losing my only living relative and my home, then it was rather won-derful to realize I could do exactly as I liked. Sometimes I felt a bit guilty – I mean, I loved Aunt Hester very dearly, but I could never have left her alone.'

'Not even to marry?'

She hesitated, her eyes reflective. 'It's strange that you should say that. Please don't laugh, but—'

'Why should I?' he interjected.

'—my childhood ambition was to be a concert pianist, but Aunt Hester disapproved strongly of anything to do with the entertainment business. I should be thinking of something safe and dependable for a career, like secretarial work, or teach-ing.'

'A predictable attitude on her part,' he observed.

Miranda gave a shrug totally without bitterness. 'In her way she was right. She said any further advanced music training would probably be a waste of money as I was bound to get married and settle down with a family.'

'So she did have marriage in mind for you.' Jason studied his cigar. 'Is that one of your ambitions now?'

'Ambition . . . that doesn't seem the right word for it.'

'What is the right word for it?' he asked idly.

She thought for a moment. 'I don't know, but ambition ex-presses a seeking for self-aims, which isn't the right attitude for marriage.'

'I suppose not.' His voice hardened. She had touched a raw spot, and resentment burned in him instantly. He sought to change the subject, but before he could speak she forestalled him.

'Marriage should be the ultimate in all human relationships,' she said softly, almost as though she spoke her thoughts aloud. 'People should take it much more seriously and unselfishly, and realize that a good relationship doesn't just happen like magic. It has to be worked for and earned like anything else.'

'Meaning that one earns and the other pays,' he said ironically.

'No,' she said firmly, 'that's based on one of the biggest misconceptions in life today – that anything worthwhile has to be bought. Love and trust can't be bought, they have to be exchanged freely. But too many people are afraid to give freely in case they don't receive in return.'

Jason glanced at her, and saw by her expression that she believed utterly in the truth of her own words. Youth's philosophy before the Fall he thought cynically, but something stopped him voicing the thought.

'There's a great deal more to it than that,' he said, smiling slightly. 'Anyway, I thought marriage was unfashionable among the young these days.'

She was silent so long he looked up and surprised the shadowy despair in her faraway gaze. 'What's the matter?' he asked. 'Only been two months in the big city and lost your illusions already?'

The blue gaze narrowed and focused back on his face, and a sigh shivered through the slender shoulders. 'Why?' she said vehemently. 'Why is it this way? Back at home it's all wrong – promiscuousness is the daddy of the seven deadly sins. Here it's a sin to be chaste. They think you're abnormal if you don't jump into bed with every man who takes you out a couple of times. Come to our place! Come to bed! Come . . .' She gave a choked little murmur and hid her face, shaking her head convulsively.

The silence was disturbing. Suddenly he felt out of his depth, and strangely shocked.

'Who are "they"?' he said at last.

'Oh, the girls I live with, and their men friends. I don't understand them and they don't understand me. All they can talk about is their wonderful freedom to live their lives the way they want to. They don't seem to understand that freedom can be as much a prison in its way as the discipline of an ordered society,' she said hotly.

'In what way?' he asked curiously, his interest caught by her

21

patent sincerity.

'Because they can be just as tyrannical to those who don't wish to conform.'

'How?'

'By their scorn and ridicule. They have their freedom; all right. They can start a relationship, and stop it as soon as they choose to. They can experiment with every new idea in living and—'

'New ideas?' he broke in. 'There aren't any. How on earth did you get mixed up with this lot?'

'I answered an advert in the agony column. You know; fourth girl wanted. It was a lovely flat, and they seemed such good fun, and I hated the hostel I stayed in for the first two weeks. Anyway, you can't stay long in the hostels. It was only a stopover until I found a permanent place.' She paused, then went on as though some long-pent-up spate had at last found release: 'Sometimes I feel the need to be on my own, to have privacy, and they accuse me of being stand-offish. If I won't join in their parties they say I'm a prude, prissy. But I have a right to my own life and my own principles. I don't try to moralize to them, so why can't they leave me alone?'

'I think you're a little too young and naïve to understand the answer to that one,' he said quietly. He leaned back and looked reflectively at her. 'Tell me, how is it that you can talk so frankly to a stranger?'

She started, and he got the impression that she was seeing him as a man for the first time. The thought piqued, and he added dryly: 'I didn't think prudish spoilsports confided so easily in strange men.'

She looked away. 'I don't think I'm prudish because I happen to have principles and resent other people belittling them.'

'I didn't mean exactly that,' he said.

She looked back at him. 'I know. But I've already told you; you're different, and you're completely impartial. That's why I told you.'

'Sure you don't mean that I'm indifferent.'

But the play on words provoked none of the response he would have expected from other women of his acquaintance. A warning instinct he never ignored told him to glance at his watch and discover that two hours had flown. He stubbed out his cigar, and instantly she took her cue from him, making it

22

plain she was ready to depart when he gave the word.

It was raining heavily when they came up to street level, and they ran the short distance to where the car was parked. After the background noise of the restaurant it seemed very quiet inside the car, only the soft patter of the rain on the windows breaking the silence.

'Well,' he said briskly, 'where now?'

She gave a small gasp of dismay. 'Oh dear! I-I'd forgotten for a little while.'

'I hadn't.' He started the car and swung out from the kerb, weaving into the stream of cars wending their way from the theatres. 'I suppose there's only one answer.'

He sensed her movement in the dimness. 'You – you're going to let me go back to the office?'

'Good heavens, no!' He grinned to himself. 'I'm going to give you a bed for the night. I don't see why I should, but—'

A horrified gasp silenced him. 'A bed? What do you mean? *Where?*'

'At my place. Where else?'

'No! But I couldn't! Thank you for – but I couldn't possibly—'

'Why not? Unless you have alternative arrangements in mind.'

He knew by the dismayed silence that she hadn't, and he said dispassionately: 'As far as I can tell you have three alternatives open to you: the perils of a permissive party, the cold, uncomfortable great outside – Piccadilly's a favourite, I believe – or the comfort of a reasonably well-appointed bachelor's pad in a highly respectable square. So what's it to be?'

'You know it can't be any of those.' She sighed despairingly. 'If only you hadn't come back tonight!'

'But I did.' He took a swift glance sideways and saw her staring ahead. Her face looked deathly pale, and a possible reason for this occurred to him, making him hover between anger and mirth. Controlling both instincts, he said sardonically: 'You don't trust me. You think I may have designs on your innocence.'

'I don't know what to think,' she said in a small bewildered voice.

'It's such a terrifying idea, isn't it?' he mocked softly.

'Terrifying isn't the right word.'

'I forget. You're such a stickler for the correct definition,

Miss Meake. Disgusting, maybe?'

'No. Just sad, I think.'

The quality of that emotion in her voice tipped the balance of his own attitude. Abruptly he braked and pulled the car to a halt. Making no effort to subdue his anger, he slewed round to face her and saw her shrink away against the passenger door.

'Don't look at me as though I were some lecher bound on a cheap thrill. I'd be the first to admit that I like women, but not to the extent you seem to suspect. When I want amusement I certainly don't find it with little scared innocents who appear to have stepped straight out of a Victorian sermon.'

She recoiled, and he drew a deep angry breath. 'Now listen, young woman, I'm giving you one last chance. Take it, or go to the devil and this great permissive city you're so scared of.'

His hands trembled as he grasped the wheel and put the car into motion again. 'There's an hotel down here. I know the manager. I'll book you in for the night where you'll be safe, and after that you're on your own. If you've any sense you'll find yourself a new home – or go back to Evesham. Kids like you should never be let loose in London in the first place.'

Suspicious sounds, as though stifled by a handkerchief, reached his ears and evoked only a renewal of irritation. 'And for God's sake try not to snivel when we go in.'

'How can I?' she wailed. 'I've no money. I told you—'

'I remember.' He turned into the quiet terrace and headed for the high dark bulk of the big building at the far end. 'I doubt if many respectable hotels would take you in minus luggage at this time of night, no matter how much money you had. I'll see to that, and if you're wise you won't argue.'

Slowly she got out of the car and lagged behind his brisk steps as he hurried up the short, tree-lined drive. Under the light of the stone portico it looked as though she might begin fresh protests, then she sighed as she looked up at him and her face closed. 'I'll repay you as soon as I can,' she said stiffly. 'Thank you for the meal, and—'

'Forget it.' Wanting only to be out of it, he escorted her inside and gave terse instructions to a somewhat surprised night porter. It took only a few minutes, and he bade her a brusque good night and escaped thankfully to his car.

By the time he reached Byrne Square he had almost but not quite succeeded in banishing Miss Miranda Meake's woebegone countenance from his mind. He rarely saw the need to analyse his impulses or his actions, except for those pertaining to the world of business, and he saw no reason to begin now. But what an odd child; he didn't think they made them like that any more. All the odder when overlaid with the glib philosophy they all had, as though they'd found the magic formula that could change the world overnight. Well, the world certainly needed something.

Jason yawned, overcome by a sudden wave of intense weariness, Monday: Bonn. Wednesday: Stockholm. Thursday back to London, and New York the following Monday ... The prospect of the next two weeks held no joy whatever. Maybe he'd be able to take a break after the American trip. He could stop-over at—

The phone interrupted his weary musing. Muttering, he reached for it, and in an instant his lassitude vanished.

'*Lissa!*'

'Surprised?'

'Very.' He released a pent-up breath. 'But I didn't—'

'I know, darling, but listen, may I come and see you?'

'Of course,' with a slightly unsteady hand he groped into the cigarette box. 'But I thought you—'

'You thought wrong, my sweet.' interrupted the soft, breathless little voice that could still wield its once extremely potent effect on his senses, 'but never mind about that – there's a most peculiar character loitering outside this booth. You see, I've been staying with Claire, but I'm home a week sooner than I planned, because James suddenly decided to have those people we met at Mummy's last Easter over for the week-end – you know what an idiot he is over a title – and he insisted that I come home.'

Jason made a sympathetic noise into the phone, even as his mouth curled with derision; James was no idiot, but he was one hell of a snob ... what the devil had Lissa ever seen in that pompous ass ...?

'So,' she went on with a sigh, 'I must obey the command. The soonest flight I could get was tomorrow afternoon, so I fixed that and phoned James to expect me then, and then not half an hour afterwards they rang to say there'd been a cancellation on this evening's flight and did I want it? I was going to say no, and then,' there was a small pause for breath, the catch of which he heard quite plainly, 'you see, Claire and I were talking about you just as the phone went – she was asking if I ever saw you these days – and so I thought . . .'

Jason found his own voice suddenly constricted. 'Yes,' he prompted.

'It – it's been such a long time,' she whispered. 'Almost a year. I've missed you so much, and I still feel guilty because I hurt you. So I thought, if I took this early flight, perhaps I could make you forgive me . . . perhaps . . . So I just came. Have I done right, my darling?'

'Don't make me answer that,' he said huskily. 'Where are you?'

'At the air terminal.'

'I'll come and get you.' His glance slid to the clock. 'I'll be about twenty—'

'No,' she broke in, 'I'll take a taxi. I should be with you very soon.'

'Have you eaten?'

'On the flight. Don't bother about anything – I just want to see you again. Oh, Jason, it's so wonderful to hear your voice again.' There was a sigh, then the sound of a kiss over the wire and a small, intimate chuckle. 'Just light the candles for me, darling, the way we used to . . .'

The soft husky voice stopped, then there was a click and the line went blank.

Jason's earlier mood had fallen from him like a dropped cloak. His heart was speeding as he hurried down to the cellar to select a bottle of wine. Quietly, he didn't want to disturb Libby on her evening off . . . Pity he had no flowers . . . come to that, there were no candles! He put out the centre light, leaving only the soft glow of the wall brackets burning, switched on a bar of the fire and glanced round the warm, inviting room.

Lissa . . .

How was it she unfailingly knew when he most needed her. . .?

CHAPTER TWO

EVEN at the hour of nine a.m. on a wet, depressing Monday morning a certain air of intrigue was rarely lacking in the staff rooms of Carona-Steele. Not a little credit for this not unusual state was due to the measure of consideration Carona-Steele had for their employees. Someone, somewhere, had realized that cold wet employees with that Monday morning feeling were liable to take a goodly portion of the morning to settle themselves into the frame of mind to earn their salaries; someone, somewhere, had also realized that no feminine member would achieve that desirable state until she was assured she looked her best. The anonymous someone had acknowledged the challenge and ordained that there must be ample facilities for coping with damp clothing, dripping brollies – and the glamour morale of the feminine section of the staff.

The fifth floor ladies' room was no exception to this policy. There were airing racks and neat lockers, and, more important, well lit mirrors, black glass make-up tables that would not have disgraced a five-star hotel, ample facilities for washing, and dispensers for tights, tissues, perfume, and everything else the modern miss might need.

'No dark ones left in my size – who the devil is supposed to keep these things loaded?' grumbled a very young voice. 'Bother! I can't go in like this!' The speaker exhibited a long slender thigh clad in punctured nylon. 'I put my finger through them and didn't have a spare pair. What am I going to do?' she wailed, when no one seemed disposed to sympathize.

'Take what's going – or go holey, darling,' advised a husky voice from the other side of the room.

The unfortunate Susan of the holey tights heaved a sigh of despair and opened her purse. Her lips moved in silent reckoning to the counting of coins, then she gave another wail. 'Damn! It'll leave me short for the day – even the cheap ones. Miranda ...? Can you lend me fifteen p.? Please ... I'll pay you back tomorrow without fail, I promise.'

She stared imploringly at Miranda through the mirror, impatient at the lack of response.

'I'll have to skip lunch – or walk home tonight if you don't,' she added urgently.

Miranda put down her comb and without speaking reached for her bag. She sorted out the coins and put them down on the black glass in front of Susan.

'Gosh – thanks!' Susan murmured fervently. 'I'm in your debt for ever.'

'How true,' said the husky voice across the room.

Susan ignored it. She got the pack of tights from the machine and hurriedly changed. When she came back to the mirror for the final scrutiny of herself Miranda was still standing there, motionless.

'They're not too bad,' Susan prattled on, 'except they've got those gathered bits instead of a proper toe. I like the shaped ones best – wish they'd put Lady-Mist in that machine. But I suppose the management make a profit on them – like everything else. No one'll kid me they— Miranda! What's the matter? You look as though you'd seen a ghost.'

'Do I?' Miranda turned away from the mirror. 'I'm just naturally pale. Are you ready, Sue?'

'Yes. I—'

'She's been looking as though the chopper was about to fall all week,' said Rena Harvey, brushing past Susan. 'What've you been up to, young Meake?'

'Nothing.' Miranda's mouth tightened as she watched the tall, svelte figure of the older woman move towards the door. Rena Harvey saw too much – and talked too much. Gripping her handbag strap too tightly, Miranda waited impatiently for her friend. Sue and her tights had broken into a conversation on which Miranda had been a shameless eavesdropper as she stood in front of the mirror. But she'd still heard enough to take the colour from her cheeks.

So *he* was back.

Miranda sat down at her desk and uncovered her typewriter. If only Rena Harvey knew how close to the truth were her teasing words! Exactly nine days had passed since that night she'd taken leave of her senses and tried to take possession of Jason Steele's office. Afterwards, during the endless week-end that followed, she'd wondered if she'd dreamt it all. His unexpected advent and furious discovery of her presence, his uncompromising threat to fire her, his surprising *volte-face* in taking her out to dinner, and its even more surprising denouement. But the waking-up in the strange hotel room the next morning had not been a dream, no matter how many times she had pinched herself during the breakfast served to her by a stolid-faced waiter, and when the receptionist blandly assured her that the bill had been taken care of.

What had prompted his strange action? A deep, latent chivalry in a man cast hard in a ruthless twentieth-century mould? A man whose amorous affairs constantly fired the curiosity of the office grapevine?

By the time the week-end had dragged past and Monday

28

morning loomed to the face Miranda's nerves were taut to snapping point. All that morning she waited for the summons that meant the end of her job, and when it had not arrived by five o'clock she had hardly dared to breathe her relief. Then she had heard that he was away. In Bonn.

So he hadn't been in at all.

On Wednesday the infallible Rena let drop that he was headed for Stockholm, that he was expected back the following day, and would be in New York the following week.

Miranda had wild thoughts of going sick on the Thursday. By the time he got back from America he might have forgotten all about her. But it needed only one second thought to pinpoint the weakness of that bright idea; all he needed to do was leave the edict. Did she think he would bother to summon her in person? Even though ... *'Before I give myself the pleasure of firing you personally and throwing you out of the building ...'*

But he had taken her out to dine. He'd turned perfectly charming – she'd never been out with a man who could be quite like that; urbane, man-of-the-world, attractive in a way that fascinated even as it secretly scared her ... He *couldn't* fire her! *Or could he?*

Miranda realized she'd typed the same paragraph a second time. With a guilty glance around to make sure she was unobserved she tore out the offending sheet and started again. She was being quite ridiculous worrying herself sick like this. Jason Steele had probably forgotten she even existed. Especially if Rena's latest tale was true.

Was it? That Mr. Frears was being transferred to the Rome office, and that it sounded more like a demotion than otherwise? And that was partly why the American trip had been postponed and why J.S. was back today. And if the latest whisper that had gone through the building like wildfire was true J.S.'s affair with screen starlet Catrina Kay was over. Kaput! And Rena said that Mr. Frears was the cause of it all. He'd actually had the nerve to poach on J.S.'s personal territory.

They said J.S. was crazy over her. That he'd squired her all over town, and that he'd once flown to Acapulco for one day to see her while she was there on location for a film. Miranda looked unseeingly at the still blank sheet in her machine. He must have wanted her pretty badly to go all the way to Mexico for *one* day. Was it true that he used to take a different girl out every night? After he'd had a disastrous affair with some debby type and really flipped his top when she married another man? But it was history now, they said, way back long before the day two months ago when Miranda began her new job as part of the giant Carona-Steele complex.

She frowned. Her train of thoughts were leaving a distaste behind them, a distaste she was strangely reluctant to acknowledge to herself in connection with J.S. Unaware that she sighed aloud, Miranda tried to banish Jason Steel from her mind and concentrate on her work. If she was going to worry about anything it ought to be the problem of finding a more congenial place to live. Perhaps the one she was going to see this evening might prove the solution . . .

But Jason Steele, despite his continued remoteness from the fifth floor of Carona-Steele, continued to haunt Miranda's waking moments. The day passed like any other working day, bringing no dread summons or ominous communication – but wouldn't it be in her salary at the month end? – and after a frugal tea at the Dine Lite she set off across town to inspect yet another desirable flatlet for sharing.

For the first time since starting her search she felt more optimistic when she rang the doorbell. The road seemed a quiet, pleasant one, and the big Edwardian house was freshly painted, neatly curtained, and without that impression of bursting at the seams with humanity. In fact, it looked as though even poor Aunt Hester might have given her grudging approval. The moment the door opened and the dark-haired woman stood there and smiled, Miranda felt even more hopeful and crossed her fingers.

Mrs. Saunders introduced herself and looked searchingly at Miranda. What she saw seemed to please her, for she smiled again, more informally, and volunteered the information that this was her first experience of letting part of her house. Her two daughters were both married now, she was a widow, and her decision had been crystallized by the fact of her niece coming to London to work and wanting somewhere to stay.

'So you would be sharing with her,' Mrs. Saunders went on, then gave an awkward gesture. 'I hope you'll forgive my saying this, but I have to be cautious. Jean's never been away from home before and my sister isn't very happy about the idea. She's convinced that every girl bound for London is automatically bound for the devil as well.'

She smiled, but Miranda's oval face remained serious. 'Yes, I quite understand. That's why I'm here. Because I'm getting a bit out of my depth where I'm living at present.'

Mrs. Saunders nodded, her dark eyes shrewd. 'Yes, it takes a while to find your feet in a strange city, especially if it's the first time you've been away from home. Would you like to see the flat?'

'Yes, please,' Miranda said eagerly.

It wasn't very large, consisting of what had been the front bedroom and dressing-room on the first floor, but it was tastefully decorated and the crisp new curtains were gay and modern. There were ample cupboards, a brand new sink unit and a bijou cooker were screened behind a light lattice partition with roomy shelves and compartments facing the lounge part of the room, and the furnishings, though unpretentious, were light and contemporary.

'You can add your own bits and pieces to please yourself,' Mrs. Saunders said, smiling.

She seemed to be waiting for some sort of comment, and Miranda hestitated. The rent was considerably less than the share she was contributing at her present place, admittedly a bigger and more luxurious flat housing four of them, but it seemed to her that a lot of expense had been entailed in Mrs. Saunders's conversion.

'It's lovely,' she said at last, 'but it seems too reasonable.'

'I've no desire to profiteer from youngsters, and as Jean's almost like family it wouldn't be right to,' Mrs. Saunders said in a matter-of-fact voice. 'And my conscience wouldn't let me charge you more for exactly the same thing. When would you like to move in?'

Miranda was filled with elation when she made her way back to the flat. The unknown Jean wasn't arriving until the following month, but Mrs. Saunders said that was no reason for Miranda to delay until then. So it was fixed; she was to move in at the week-end, and even though she knew nothing except what Mrs. Saunders had told her of her prospective flatmate, instinct told her she was going to be able to manage her life with a great deal less interference in future.

But it was with some trepidation she faced breaking the news to Jane, Vanda and Louise, and for the first time she realized that she was afraid of them. They had all been curious about where she had gone the night of their party, and though she hadn't been able to resist telling them she had been out to dine with a man she had steadfastly refused to divulge his identity. It was doubtful if they'd have believed her, and the resultant interrogation would have been unbearable, but she could not help wondering what they would have said had she told them the whole truth about that night.

However, her fears were groundless about their reaction to her decision. Louise was uncaring about anything except her own affairs at the moment; Vanda was in a mood to tease and pry; only Jane betrayed temper and grumbled at the prospect of having to find a new fourth girl. But it seemed Vanda knew a model who was dissatisfied with her present abode and might be interested.

'She'd better be,' said Jane, 'or we'll have to ask you to pay up for another month. After all, we didn't ask you to go,' she added unpleasantly.

Miranda could have made a pertinent retort to that, but she kept silent, thankful that one problem at least was solved.

It proved a busy week, and it passed with surprising speed. Perhaps Susan would come along on Saturday and give her a hand with the move, she thought she'd *walk* with the stuff before she'd ask the other three to help . . .

Susan was quite excited at the prospect of the move when Miranda broached the subject on the Thursday morning.

'I was wondering what you were going to do,' she said, 'and I'd have offered like a shot. But I thought the others were bound to be helping and I didn't want to get in the way. Besides, you're so darned independent,' she added wryly.

'I don't feel it – thanks a lot. You're a pal,' Miranda said fervently, 'I'll do the same for you some day. Only I'm a bit worried. I've booked a taxi and it'll be all right if it's a friendly cabbie, but it'll be just my luck to draw one who's in a bad mood and there I'll be, dropping bits and pieces all over the place.'

Susan giggled. 'My sister once left a case in a taxi. She was going to a party and staying at her friend's house overnight, and she'd packed her day things that she'd want for work the next day. She didn't realize what she'd done until the taxi had gone, and she couldn't remember the number. She wasted half the party on the phone, trying to track down the driver – it was one of those one-man affairs out in the suburbs – and when she did she found he'd gone off on a long run out into the wilds somewhere. She had frightful visions of going to work the next morning in a gold lurex trouser suit and then—'

Miranda wasn't listening. She had stopped, and was staring across the main lobby.

J.S. was coming out of the lift.

He strode forward without looking to left or right. The stream of employees, some hurrying, some lagging, seemed to melt aside from the straight path he made towards the main doors.

Miranda did not know she was turning, watching the tall, superlatively clad figure with eyes that were wide, or that her lips had parted and her entire mien betrayed that temporarily she was far from Susan's rambling little anecdote.

The doors closed smoothly behind J.S. The bright morning sunlight caught the glints of silver in the streaks at his temples, making them accentuate the thick dark springy hair that refused to be sleeked entirely out of a tendency to ruffle. Why does a touch of steel in a man's hair makes him even more attractive? Miranda wondered inconsequently, while most women dread its appearance as a telltale of age. He had paused to speak to someone, just beyond the huge abstract sculpture of steel that stood in the centre of the forecourt. She couldn't see his car. Was he going away? Because there was something—

'Miranda! What on earth's the matter with you?'

'Nothing. I—' She dragged herself back to normality and forced a careless giggle as she gave her attention to Susan.

Inwardly her thoughts still turned to J.S. and a certain problem which had come to nag her conscience now that the fear of the falling axe had diminished. It was the problem of her debt to Jason Steele. Perhaps it was of little consequence to J.S. himself, a man who seemed to think nothing of taking a day trip to Acapulco to see his girl-friend, but it was of considerable consequence to Miranda's fiercely independent spirit. What was she going to do about that hotel bill?

Although it had been a quiet, rather old-fashioned hotel its tariff had not been exeactly a cheap one, at least not to Miranda's way of thinking. If she'd had enough money on her she would have insisted on settling the bill herself, but she hadn't, and she still felt the tremor of that moment when she approached the hotel receptionist after breakfast. It had not been easy, but it was the only way to convince herself that J.S. had actually booked her in less than ten hours before, and that they would not demand payment. But her fears were quite groundless and she could laugh at herself now when she remembered the receptionist shaking her beautifully coiffured head and murmuring that she trusted Miss Meake had been comfortable . . .

Late that afternoon Miranda came to a decision, and before she could think better of it she found herself in the lift, pressing the button for the twenty-first floor.

Long before it stopped, bringing that disturbing rush in her stomach, she was tense with uncertainty. The cloistered stillness and the moss-springy feel of the carpet underfoot were instantly familiar, as were the white walls and the glass doors of the outer reception room. She could see that other door, the door to that burgundy and white office in which . . . Miranda swallowed hard and prepared to meet the haughty stare of Miss Mayo, who was already rising from her desk and advancing to deal with the invader.

J.S.'s secretary was reputed to be infallible as well as unflappable. No one knew her age, regarding which guesses ranged from forty to sixty, or a single detail of her private life. Some said she maintained an invalid father; others that she was actually married but believed in keeping personal and business lives apart, still wilder surmises had it that she was J.S.'s father's ex-mistress and had promised the old man on his deathbed that she would keep a guiding hand on the reins of Carona-Steele as long as his son needed her. Whatever the truth might be, no one had a hope of by-passing her except on the order of J.S. himself, certainly not a little typist from far below on the fifth floor.

She eyed Miranda, a cool half-smile of inquiry not reaching her eyes as she waited for the stammered question.

'Mr. Steele is in conference,' she said in crisp, off-putting tones. 'Is it important?'

'Well, it's—' Miranda bit her lip. She had not bargained for so unyielding a barrier. After all, they were all part of the same set-up; where was the reasonable camaraderie that existed among most of the staff she knew?

Already Miss Mayo had lost patience. 'If you leave the message I'll see that he has it the moment he's free.' She flashed the cool smile again, inviting the necessary communication with the confidence of one who has long coped with every exigency the business world could throw up, from blustering high-powered tycoons to apparently half-witted errand girls who seemed unable even to carry a straight message.

Suddenly Miranda's courage failed her. 'I'll – I'll tell Mr. – I'll tell him to ring up,' she got out, and scurried towards the lift before the she-guardian could call her back.

Luck, however, came when she least expected it. The next day she was waiting her turn to be served with her lunch-time coffee and sandwiches in the staff cafeteria when the phone rang. The voice of the unseen girl who answered behind the frosted glass partition was quite shrill and audible: A tray. Black coffee. Ham rolls. Fruit. At one sharp. For Mr. Steele.

He must be staying in for lunch. But what about the she-guardian?

He'd send her for her lunch at the same time, surely, Miranda decided. It was a pity she was due back herself at one, but it couldn't be helped. The manner of this debt had assumed enormous proportions and she had to settle it. She returned to her desk as usual at one o'clock, and waited until ten past. Then she took the five-pound note already secreted in her desk drawer, glanced round to see if anyone was watching, and slipped quietly from the office. The lift was waiting, empty, and the twenty-first floor appeared deserted when she stepped out a few moments later. She peered through the glass doors and sighed with relief to see the outer room of the suite was empty. The formidable Miss Mayo *must* be out to lunch – unless she was sharing it with J.S.

Breathing a prayer that she wasn't – strangely, the thought of the secretary made Miranda more nervous than the thought of J.S. himself – she tiptoed into the outer room and across to the white door. She listened, then raised a hand that trembled slightly.

Her knuckles met the white panel and at that precise moment the door opened. Miranda gasped, and only just managed to stop herself falling through.

Jason Steele took an involuntary step back and put out a defensive hand. For a second they stared at one another, then he was the first to recover. He said: 'Well?' in a peremptory tone, and continued to stare at her with eyes which held not a vestige of recognition.

'I – I—' Miranda gulped, her nerve almost failing her, and gave him a pleading look. 'You don't remember me, Mr. Steele, but you – I'm the girl—'

35

The prepared speech deserted her and she trailed into a flummoxed silence. When he looked like that he positively intimidated. She'd forgotten how tall he was close to, how broad his shoulders, how hard and determined the line of his jaw, and most of all she had forgotten the sheer forceful male dominance of him. Plainly he'd forgotten she ever existed; how foolish her concern, and how unfounded her fear of dismissal that had haunted her all last week.

She took a deep breath. 'Mr. Steele – I'm sorry to interrupt your lunch, but I wanted to—'

'It's little Miss Meake!'

His mocking recognition ignored her endeavour to begin explanations. He stepped back and indicated the office behind him. 'Won't you come in, Miss Meake?'

Her eyes betraying her uncertainty, she walked into the burgundy and white room that was more like a luxuriously furnished lounge than an office.

He waved to the settee she'd once planned to sleep on and said dryly: 'What can I do for you this time, Miranda Meake?'

'Nothing.' Without taking her eyes off him she sank down into the rich burgundy upholstery. 'I've been trying to see you all this week. I—'

'Really!' he broke in. 'Am I so elusive?'

'No, but . . .' It was proving more difficult than she had anticipated; he seemed in a mood to make fun of her. The thought stiffened her and her head went up. 'I wanted to thank you, that's all.'

'Whatever for?' A flicker of surprise lifted his brows. 'Do you mind if I continue my lunch?'

'Oh no! I'm sorry,' she exclaimed, instantly remorseful. 'I wouldn't have interrupted, but it was the only way I could catch you alone. You see, I wanted to give you this,' she rushed on, standing up and unfolding the crumpled note that was turning limp in her warm clutch. 'I hope it's enough – but I don't know the exact amount. And I'd just like to say thank you, and I appreciate very much what you did but I can't possibly let you pay for it.' In her anxiety, she leaned over the desk. 'If it isn't enough please tell me.'

'What on earth are you talking about?' He stared at her. 'And what's this?' He eyed the crumpled note she'd laid on his desk.

'It's for the hotel bill.'

'Oh.' He leaned back, and now there was an expression in his eyes that made her falter. He reached out and with a single contemptuous flick of his fingers sent the note sliding across the polished surface towards her. 'I seemed to remember telling you to forget it.'

'Yes, I know. But I can't.'

'Perhaps you would like me to remember a few other things,' he said dryly.

She gazed back wordlessly, and a slight smile curled his mouth.

'I remember now that I was going to fire you.'

She made a small movement of her shoulders. Perhaps it conveyed a more fatalistic attitude than she knew, or perhaps a carelessness that piqued him.

'Haven't you heard of sleeping dogs?' he asked.

The soft catch of her breath was audible. She looked down. 'I had to offer to repay you, I can't help it. It seemed the least I could do.'

He shrugged. 'Take it. I don't want your savings.'

'But—'

'I warn you, if it litters my desk I shall merely toss it in the waste-paper basket.'

'You would throw money away?'

He glanced up at her shocked expression and laughed unexpectedly. 'Miranda Meake, I must warn you: I am not used to losing arguments.'

'I can see that.' Unhappily, she regarded the despised note and then looked at him with a gaze more appealing than she knew. 'Honestly, Mr. Steele, I've no desire to argue with you, and certainly not to make you angry.'

'I wonder.' Idle speculation came into his face. 'Your temperament must suffer constantly from that unfortunate handicap.'

'What handicap?'

'The confliction of that streak of stubbornness in your nature and the odd little quirk of meekness your name has undoubtedly bestowed on you. I wonder which it is? Did the name invoke the stubbornness in sheer self-defence? Or did the subconscious decide that meekness must not win so easy a victory? Meake by name . . .?'

'And meek by nature?' Her mouth tightened. 'That is unfair

37

as well as unkind. I *could* voice an equally unfair surmise concerning yourself, Mr. *Steele*.'

For a moment she thought the hammers of wrath were about to descend on her defenceless head, then abruptly he leaned back and laughed aloud.

'*Touché!*' He indicated the tray. 'Would you like a cup of coffee?'

'No, thank you. Anyway, there's only one cup.'

'Ho ho! Defeatist. My secretary is prepared for all emergencies – the cupboard under her small filing cabinet in the outer office has nothing whatsoever to do with Carona-Steele.' He gestured lazily. 'Take a look. You'll find spare cups, among the instant coffee and the assortment of patent medicines she hoards in there.'

Miranda was tempted, but she shook her head. 'I'd better not – I've had my lunch hour and I'll be missed by now.'

'I don't qualify as a valid excuse for your being missing?' He sounded amused.

She regarded him steadily. 'No. Because it was really a personal matter.'

His head inclined to one side as he considered that, his expression unreadable. Rather abruptly he stood up and lounged round the side of the desk. 'Yes, I suppose it is. Very personal.' His eyes mocking, he picked up the banknote between his fingertips. 'A matter of debt and honour and all that. I never expected to hear of it again.'

'You mean you thought I'd just accept it and not even bother to offer repayment?' She looked shocked.

'Something like that.'

'But I couldn't!' She looked even more horrified. 'Especially after what I did . . . and you didn't even know me.'

'Does that matter?' He smiled slightly. 'You happened to provide a diversion I needed badly that evening, so it isn't quite as one-sided as you imagine.'

Her eyes widened. 'I don't understand.'

'You don't have to, little Miss Meake, just forget to argue.'

Still she stared at him, an odd little sense of hurt stealing upon puzzlement. A diversion . . . what did he mean?

A gleam came into his eyes and the cynical quirk played round his lips. 'I'd forgotten your idealistic sentiments – and it makes me begin to suspect the real cause of the fuss. You fled an orgy that night,' he said in a way that made her feel he thought her a ridiculous young innocent, 'and ended up having a man pay for your bed and board. A lonely, virginal bed that the most ardent moralist could not take exception to. Yes, I agree, a most unsatisfactory state of affairs. I can see you have cause for concern.'

This unexpected accusation took her by surprise. Before she could frame an adequate retort he moved forward and put his hand on her shoulders. He looked down into her startled face, gave a slight shake of his head.

'But I dislike having my attempts at chivalry thrown back in my face, and so I'm going to have the last word.'

Before she realized his intent or could protest he had flicked the note under her nose and then, with an impudent flourish, dropped it down the neck of her neat white blouse.

He stepped back and glanced at his watch. 'Isn't it time you returned to your work, Miss Meake?' he said coolly.

CHAPTER THREE

MIRANDA felt strangely reluctant to spend, or bank, that somewhat tattered fiver. Whenever she thought of the incident and her furtive flight into the ladies' to retrieve the folded note from where it had amused J.S. to deposit it she felt a wave of pink highlight her cheeks, and his dark rakish features persisted in floating about in her mind.

It was all quite ridiculous, she told herself crossly. She had obeyed the honesty of conscience, he had chosen to be derisive about it, so that was the end of the matter. The more she thought about it the plainer it became that she had been an embarrassment to him that evening, and he had been quite frank in his turn; she had been a diversion. Otherwise, it was highly improbable that he would have taken her out to dine, after which the awkwardness had come and he had settled it in his imperious way and forgotten about the matter. But far from forgetting it herself she found the memories of that evening becoming more vivid instead of dimming with time. The three alternatives he had suggested . . . How naïve she must have seemed in her reaction when he suggested taking her back to his home. And yet what else was she to assume? Other than the obvious from a man of his reputation? For there had to be some truth in what the grapevine said, even if it were only a grain. She *would* be naïve if she believed that J.S. was a saint where women were concerned. For one thing, he was too attractive; for another he was possessed of all the material trappings wealth and position could supply, and for the third reason, of which Miranda disliked intensely to think, there were a lot of girls to whom those very material trappings mattered more than the actual man who owned them . . . she only hoped she'd made it quite plain that *she* wasn't one of them.

The move to her new flat almost but not quite banished the troublesome shade of J.S. for a little while, and at least kept her spare time fully occupied that week-end and the few days following while she arranged things neatly. Conscientious as always, she was careful not to take an inch more than her half share of the cupboard and shelf space, and she purposely left most of it blank in the living-room she would be sharing with Jean. When Jean arrived they would plan things together, decide whose personal possessions would go where and if they should keep the little shelves at the sides of the gas fire for books or dress them with something more trendy. What would Jean be like? Would she be friendly? Quiet and serious, or gay and fun-loving? I hope she likes folk music and ballet, Miranda thought . . .

By the Thursday she was beginning to feel quite at home. She had written to everyone she could think of to tell them her new address, and she had organized the bijou kitchen for the optimum of speed in getting breakfast in the morning; there was nothing more she could do until Jean came.

But there was one thing she had forgotten, and on the Friday afternoon she was reminded of it rather forcibly.

Rena Harvey herself came into the office to deliver the message and gave Miranda a peculiar look.

'What *have* you been up to this time, my girl?'

'N-nothing,' Miranda gulped.

'And what do you mean – this time?' Susan put in from across the room, looking at Rena.

'What's it about?' Miranda asked, getting up from her desk and feeling unexpectedly tremulous at the knees.

'How should I know?' Rena responded pertly. 'J.S. doesn't inform all and sundry about his business. Now go on, Miranda, for goodness' sake don't keep him waiting.'

Miranda's palms were quite clammy as she went up in the

lift. She brushed nervously at an errant strand of hair and wondered what lay in store. What *had* she done that J.S. should
summon her to the pinnacle of power? He never sent down for
anyone except chief executives. Surely after all this time he
wasn't going to ... And he couldn't have changed his mind
about that five pounds!

She tried to laugh to herself, but it came out more like a
hollow little groan that caused the only other occupant of the
lift – a rotund, elderly man – to glance at her sharply. She
hadn't meant any sound to escape her, and he was too shy of
young females to make any comment, so she gave an embarrassed shake of her head in response to the look which plainly
wondered if she was feeling all right. He got out at the eight-
eenth floor, bound no doubt for Records, and Miranda pressed
the button with a trembling finger to continue her journey
upwards.

Miss Mayo was in possession. She favoured Miranda with a
lacquered smile that told her nothing and nodded towards the
white door. 'Go straight through, Miss Meake.'

Miranda tapped and obeyed, closing the door soundlessly
behind her and staying within reach of its support.

He was standing by the window and for a moment she
thought he hadn't heard her enter. Then without turning his
head he said: 'Sit down, Miss Meake.'

It was an innocuous enough command, but it did nothing to
relax her tension. The nearest seat was the deep, white and
burgundy tub chair that matched the three-seater, and it
seemed a long way across the expanse of heavy grey carpet.
'You sent for me, Mr. Steele,' she said uneasily.

'Yes.'

Without haste, he crossed the room and seated himself in his
desk chair. He swivelled till he faced her and leaned back
coolly.

'Why have you failed to inform us of your change of
address?' he rapped out so sharply she started with alarm.

'M-my change of address?' she said foolishly. 'I – I—'

'It's one of the corporation rules that all, I repeat all, our
employees must inform Records of any change of address in
their place of permanent residence.'

'But I didn't . . .' She bit her lip on the word know and stared
at him with dismayed eyes. That wasn't true; she did know, but
she had forgotten the vaguely absorbed terms and instructions

41

she had received at the start of her employment with Carona-Steele. And she had racked her brains last week trying to ensure that she'd left nobody off her list of people to inform.

'I'm sorry, Mr. Steele,' she said guiltily. 'I forgot. I – I'll go straight away now and tell them.'

She stood up as she spoke, but he raised one hand. 'I haven't finished yet, Miss Meake.'

She sank back into the chair. Now the racket was going to start. Why did these things always happen to her?

'When did you move?'

'Only last Saturday.' She seized eagerly at mitigation. 'I've only been there five and a half days. I'm sure I'd have remembered to put the record straight very soon.'

He gave a gesture of disinterest. 'Where is it?'

'Syrian Lane – just off Willow Grove. It's a bit farther out, but it's nice,' she volunteered.

'How many others in the warren?' he asked dryly.

'None – it belongs to a lady whose family have all grown up and got married. The house is too big for her on her own and when her niece wrote and said she was coming to London to work as soon as she finished school Mrs. Saunders had the idea of making part of the upstairs into a flat for her and getting another girl to share it. So her son-in-law did most of the conversion for her,' Miranda rushed on eagerly, thankful that apparently the stormclouds were not to descend after all. 'And it's really super.'

'Super.' His mouth curved with ironic amusement. 'What a revolting little word that is!'

'Well, very nice,' she amended.

'And not likely to cause you to resort to my office for emergency accommodation?'

She couldn't meet the expression in his eyes and she looked down. 'I don't think so.'

The intercom on his desk buzzed softly and he flicked down the switch. Miss Mayo's voice came through, faintly metallic, and J.S. said crisply: 'I'll be free in a moment, put him through.' He looked up at Miranda. 'Go to Records now before you forget again.'

He was coldly impersonal again, and with a murmured assent she got up hastily. As bid, she went straight to the long glass-panelled department that housed the records and insurance cards of every member of the staff, and somehow wasn't surprised to meet again the rotund man who had shared the lift on the journey upwards. Pedantically, he noted her new address, asked if there was a phone number, and said 'Thank you – that's all,' as she still hesitated.

'Er – was Mr. Steele very angry?' she asked anxiously.

'Mr. Steele?' The elderly man frowned. 'Angry?'

'When he found I hadn't told you?'

He still looked puzzled. 'What are you talking about, miss? Mr. Steele doesn't have time to bother about things like that.'

'No, I only wondered if – when he—' She shook her head, decidedly flustered by now, and made her escape before the elderly man had time to become more curious.

She was thoughtful when she returned to her own desk and so vague that the undisguised curiosity of Susan and the other girls in the department failed to register.

'But what did he *want*?' Susan persisted.

'Nothing.'

'Nothing? We thought you were up for the chopper at least.'

'Oh, there was something wrong with my record card,' she mumbled.

'And J.S. sent for you because of *that*? Pull the other one!'

'He did – if you don't believe me go and ask him yourself Miranda retorted.

No one seemed inclined to follow this suggestion and Miranda was allowed to resume her work. It was not until she was home that night that the puzzling piece fell into place.

If Records hadn't known she'd moved, how had J.S.?

*   *   *

It was a question that seemed doomed to going unanswered. The following Monday held that slight relaxing of pressure which comes when the top man is missing. The news that he'd left that morning for the postponed American trip filtered down through the building and reached Accounts by ten o'clock. The slackening did not last long as the promotion-seekers near the top of the pyramid flexed their authority and schemed how best the week ahead could be utilized to further personal ambition. But to Miranda there was a curious empti-ness about the place. J.S.'s absence made no difference to her working routine, and while as often as not weeks could go by

43

when he *was* in the building without her ever seeing him it was rather odd that she should be so conscious of this flatness in the atmosphere, as though something vital were missing . . .

She wished she could say casually to Rena: 'When's the Great White Chief coming back?' but knew she dared not. Rena hadn't missed that surprising summons to the summit. Her eyes had been openly speculative and Miranda's vagueness hadn't satisfied her curiosity. She might respond with carelessness, depending on her mood at the moment, but she was far more likely to round on Miranda and demand the reason for this sudden interest in J.S.'s movements.

Not for the first time Miranda wondered about Rena. Were the rumours true about her and 'Money' Travers, as the chief accountant was disrespectfully known? He was a dry-looking man, with one of those soft voices you had to strain to hear or you didn't catch what he was saying. He was quite oldish too. Older than Rena, who guarded her age jealously. She was a tall, flamboyant woman with gipsy-dark hair and eyes, and a wide mouth she emphasized rather than played down with vivid scarlet lipstick. But she could wear exciting clothes with a panache many of the younger girls secretly envied, despite their tendency to giggle behind her back. Somehow, Miranda mused, one imagined her with a more exciting man, and after all, Money Travers was very much married. His wife always attended the company functions, and every Tuesday she had some engagement or other in town, after which she met him at the office and they went home together. Those were the only times when Rena tended to merge with the background. Miranda sighed: it was none of her business . . .

By midweek she hadn't time to think about J.S., let alone the rest of the office intrigues.

One of those unpleasant bugs vaguely classified as gastric 'flu hit the Carona-Steele staff.

Rena was one of the first to succumb, and with several others had to be sent home at lunchtime. By Wednesday there were more blank desks than occupied, and by the end of the week only a skeleton of the staff remained unstricken. The lucky escapers tended to doubt their luck as they coped with their own work and tried to spread the burden of the victims.

Miranda and Susan both volunteered to stay late again on the Friday night, but at eight o'clock Susan suddenly complained of feeling sick. Ray Desdon, a pleasant boy who had joined the firm only a few weeks before, offered to run her home. Susan protested wanly because it would leave Miranda alone in the department, whereupon Ray extended the offer to include Miranda.

She shook her head, knowing that Ray was attracted to Susan but too shy to risk a snub. This could be his chance to start the friendship he desired.

'I'll come back for you,' he said awkwardly. 'I don't like to pack in and leave you.'

'No, just look after Susan,' she said firmly. 'I'm just going to get this lot into the post and then I'm off.'

She worked on alone after they'd gone and heaved a tired sigh of relief when the last sheet rattled out of the machine. She flexed her weary shoulders and glanced at the clock. Nearly nine! Heavens! Quickly she got her coat, not bothering to make hasty make-up repairs, and grabbed the big pile of stuff for the post.

Most of the floors were in darkness by now, but here and there lights showed where others still strove to complete the week's schedule. The cleaning staff had long since gone, and the night guard was standing by the lift entrance when Miranda descended to ground level. He was talking to a grey-headed man whom Miranda knew by sight, and the dog was there, sitting quietly yet watchful. The men nodded, with a rueful 'Late again tonight, miss,' and she felt the dog's gaze follow her as she crossed to the big glass doors. She was sure it remembered her from 'that' night and knew that it had been an occasion of infinitely nefarious presence! Well, its sagacious reasoning would be tested to the full this week, she smiled to herself, as she heard voices from unseen persons somewhere to her left along the forecourt and a car door slamming in the darkness on the right.

She hurried across and out into the road. There was a pillar box at the corner where she would get rid of the mail and then she could go home. How was Susan . . .? It wasn't very serious, the bug, unpleasant and uncomfortable the three or four days it knocked you, but it didn't leave the ghastly aftermath that 'flu did. Or so they said. She'd have to go shopping for new shoes tomorrow and a few things, but on Sunday she'd go over and visit Susan . . .

The pillar box was almost full. Several other departments of Carona-Steele had got there first. Miranda stuffed her load in and swore as she dropped several of them. The big ones should have gone along the post office, but that would be shut now . . .

The sweeping brilliance of headlights outlined her as she stooped to gather up the fallen packets. She caught the glare in her eyes as she straightened and muttered as she blinked hastily and turned away. Brakes and tyres made the rushing swish of a car pulling up suddenly as she manoeuvred the last large envelope into the box, and a voice said:

'Have you just finished?'

Startled, she spun round to see the burgundy Mercedes at the kerb and J.S. looking from the window.

She was too surprised to do anything but nod and exclaim: 'I didn't know you were back!'

'Didn't you?' A trace of amusement flitted over his face at the pleasure she did not know she had betrayed. 'You must have missed me,' he added dryly.

A sudden wave of confusion washed over her and made it impossible to meet this statement with equanimity. She could only look down, and an odd expression flickered in his eyes for a moment, to vanish as quickly as it came. His usual cool assumption was back in his peremptory order:

'Get in. I'll run you home.'

He opened the car door as he spoke, and she stared at him.

'Thank you, but . . .' Shyness kept her standing where she was, even as weariness made its instant urge not to miss this chance before it disappeared.

'Don't argue – it's been one hell of a day.'

Silently she got in, and without speaking he pulled away quickly. He seemed to have no doubts about directions, and when she turned shyly and ventured a suggestion he said coolly:

'I remember: Syrian Lane, off Willow Grove.'

Feeling snubbed, she said, 'I'm sorry – this must be taking you miles out of your way.'

'You don't know my way.'

There seemed no response she could make to this curt little statement, other than a return to the retreat of silence. She did not venture to leave it, and the snubbed feeling was nurtured by the silence until it became distinct hurt. When the car swung into the long tree-lined road and Jason Steele asked: 'Which turning?' Miranda replied in a choked little voice: 'Second on the right – fourth house along,' and stared steadily in front of her.

46

He made the turn and slid to a smooth halt at the fourth gate. Before she could grasp her bag and prepare to get out he cut the engine and flicked on the roof light, illuminating her small set face.

'What's the matter?' he said quietly.

'Nothing. Thank you for—'

His hand came down on her arm. 'I told you, Miranda, it's been a hell of a day. Don't you remember – no arguing?' he reminded her in the same quiet tone.

'I have no intention of arguing.' She tried to keep her voice steady and expressionless. 'Nor did I ask you to give me this lift.'

His eyes closed with impatience, then he sighed. 'Don't you know that polite protestations are one of the most pointless and irritating forms of argument?' His grasp slackened and he shook his head. 'All right. You wanted to be polite and I just wanted the quiet darkness of the car and to get the whine of those accursed jets out of my head.' He sighed. 'I'm sorry, I didn't mean to be rude.'

'Oh – but I didn't know!' She turned quickly to look at him. 'I mean, I didn't understand. Have you just come from the airport?'

'Practically – I got in a couple of hours ago.'

She studied him in silence for a moment, and now she saw the tautness of weariness round his mouth and the shadowed hollows over tired eyes. A rush of compassion made her forget the snub, whether it was real or fancied, and want to assuage that utter exhaustion glimpsed in his face. Without stopping to think she said impulsively: 'I *would* have argued if I'd known that – would you like some coffee?'

His brows went up. 'Here?'

'Yes – it'll only take me a minute to make some.'

Her eyes were wide now with a quaint mixture of concern and eagerness in their depths, and suddenly he smiled. 'I'd love some.'

'Well, then . . .' She smiled back at him and looped her bag and carrier over her arm. She turned and fumbled for the car door handle, a strange excitement making her movements quick and jerky. Thank goodness she'd grabbed a few oddments during her lunch hour, and the cupboard wasn't quite bare. And thank goodness Jean hadn't . . . She scrambled out, sheering away from that gleeful thought concerning the absence of her prospective flatmate. Had she left the place tidy when she came away this morning? It seemed such a long time since she'd set off for the office . . .

The ground floor was in darkness. Mrs. Saunders must be out, she thought, conscious of another rush of delight as she opened the front door and groped inside for the light-switch before she glanced back at J.S.

'My place is on the first floor,' she said, waiting until he closed the outer door.

She saw his gaze rove the neat hallway with its white paint-work, rose-red carpet, and the rosewood occasional table which Mrs. Saunders kept polished like a mirror. But he made no comment and followed her up to the flat, appearing not to notice as she furtively shoved a small froth of blue lace and nylon under a cushion. She'd meant to sew the broken strap of the slip last night and forgotten it, so she'd left it out so that she wouldn't forget tonight. Apart from that the flat was neat and spotless.

Somehow the room seemed smaller when he was standing in the centre of it. She switched on the fire and said rather shyly: 'Please sit down, Mr. Steele – I'll make the coffee.' She flitted to the opening in the room divider, then stopped. 'Would you like something to eat? A Danish sandwich, or something on toast? Or I could make an omelette – I usually make something for myself at this time if I'm not out,' she rushed on rather feverishly.

'Don't make anything special for me – just the coffee or whatever you're having,' he said from the depths of the arm-chair.

She stood for a moment in the tiny kitchenette, then set to work briskly. Perhaps it took her considerably longer than the 'minute' originally stated, but the tray looked very attractive when she finished a quite reckless raid on her small store. The open sandwiches of salami topped with tomato rings, sliced cucumber, egg and cress looked all right – what if he didn't like cucumber? She'd better leave one without it – and it was lucky she'd bought those cheese straws to nibble herself. She hesitated over the cherry cake; better not. She'd had it since last week-end and though it seemed all right it might be a bit sandy by now. Anyway, men didn't go for sweet stuff very much . . . She put the coffee-pot on the tray and carried it carefully into the lounge.

48

'Good heavens – is this a party?' He stared at her handiwork. 'Who's going to eat all this?'

She shrugged. 'Black or white?'

'Black, please.'

Despite his casual response about 'just coffee' a few minutes previously, he helped himself to the salami specials three times and quite a few cheese straws. He seemed disinclined to make small talk, and Miranda was content to sit in the other chair and sip her coffee in silence. Presently he moved and reached for the coffee-pot, and instantly she sprang up.

He waved her down and refilled his cup, then leaned back and regarded her somewhat enigmatically.

'I take it there are no rules here about entertaining gentlemen friends,' he said dryly.

'I don't know – this is the first time.' She looked down, then up at him. 'But you're my boss,' she said simply.

He pulled a face. 'That making a difference, I suppose.'

She gave a small shake of her head and stared down into her cup. There was a sense of unreality in having J.S. sitting there, sharing a hastily rustled-up meal and leaning his head back as he rubbed the tips of finger and thumb into tightly closed eyes. The brief gesture betrayed the tiredness she had noticed before, then he blinked and gave her an unexpectedly sweet smile.

'I enjoyed that – it's brought me back to life.'

'I'm glad.' She put the dishes on the tray, murmured, 'I'll get rid of these,' and took the tray into the kitchenette. There, she set it down on the tiny bench, intending to return to the fireside and her guest, but she stayed where she was, staring unseeingly at the dishes.

It was strange the way things happened when one least expected them, and it was impossible not to feel a little awe of J.S., but she could not help wishing she had known this undreamed-of meeting was going to happen. She hadn't even stopped to tidy her hair or touch up her make-up before she left the office, and she would have preferred to have been wearing something crisp and fresh instead of this pink thing that was plainly tired after a twelve-hour day . . .

She sighed and looked at herself in the small mirror on the ledge of the partition. It was doubtful if J.S. noticed or cared whether she looked bandbox fresh; he looked dead on his feet tonight. She sighed again and went back into the main room.

It was strangely silent, and when she reached the fireside she knew why: J.S. had succumbed to the warmth of the fire and exhaustion. He was sound asleep.

For a moment Miranda looked down at him, expecting those grey eyes to flash open, but they didn't, and she bit her lip, framing the words to rouse him. They didn't come, and after a further hesitation she sank down into her own chair. It was almost impossible not to study him now that there seemed no risk of meeting that disconcerting smoke-grey stare or the sardonic twist of his mouth that invariably preceded his quelling pronouncements, and she gave full rein to the desire to search those dark, well-defined features with their hint of saturnity which could attract as easily as they commanded – or subdued. Yes, they betrayed a strength of will and ruthlessness that could intimidate a weaker nature, she thought; they also conveyed a certain magnetism he would not hesitate to use in order to get his own way. But now, in repose, he looked younger and strangely defenceless, and she had the strange sensation of a switch of power, as though she were in command . . .

A silly little fancy! She smiled to herself and reached for her library book on the shelf behind her chair. She would read quietly and let him rest for a short while, then she would tiptoe into the kitchenette and do those few dishes. The sounds would wake him and he wouldn't realize any time had passed . . . With the instinctive knowledge that this would spare him any embarrassment, she opened her book and began to read . . .

But it didn't work out quite according to plan. She found it difficult to keep her attention off him and on her book, and she was sitting in her own light which didn't make reading very easy. At last she simply let the book rest on her lap while she stared at the glow of the fire and let her thoughts wander where they would. Where did he live? He wasn't married . . . who looked after him? Did he have a large house with a staff or did he live in one of those fabulously expensive penthouses where you simply rang a bell for service? She stole another look at him. Were the stories true, the tales that were bandied along the office grapevine? Was he a womanizer? Wat it true he broke off an affair the moment the girl started getting serious? But they pursued him, or so Rena said, and if they hadn't enough sense to learn the rules they'd only themselves to blame if they got hurt . . . But what rules . . .? Surely the ultimate was a full and enduring relationship . . . a thing of love . . . not a continual hopping from one affair to another that left emotional dissatisfaction and a bruised heart in its wake . . .

In that strange way of it, sleep came to Miranda without her knowing it. Her head drooped and turned against the cushion, much as Jason Steele's had turned against the wing of the high-backed chair at the other side of the fireside. She did not hear the sound of a door closing downstairs – the house was too sturdily built and Edwardian in its size for much sound to penetrate – nor did she hear the flurries of rain begin to beat on the window and the stormy wind stir through the plane tree that cast its branching shadow against the front of the house. She slept on until her book slid from her lap and landed against her toes, bringing her awake with a start.

She sat up, momentarily still out of touch with reality, then saw Jason Steele regarding her with disturbing steadiness.

'Why didn't you wake me?' He moved, snapping back to life with a brusqueness she might have expected and stretching his wrist free of his cuff. 'Good God!' he exclaimed. 'Look at the time, girl!'

Already her dismayed glance had sought her own wristwatch and looked at it unbelievingly. It couldn't be one o'clock! He stood up and was staring at her accusingly.

'I – I'm sorry,' she faltered. 'I didn't realize . . . I went to sleep myself, and—'

'Yes, but surely.' He slicked his hair back with impatient hands, and settled his tie, making an irritable movement of his head as he did so. Your hospitality was very pleasant, but do you always let your guests sleep it off?'

'No.' She looked down. 'But you seemed very weary. I – I hadn't the heart to wake you up,' she added in a low voice.

The expected riposte did not come. Instead he shot her a sharp glance. 'That was very thoughtful of you, Miss Meake, and I do appreciate it, but I dislike the thought of causing you inconvenience, especially after what has been, by all the accounts I heard earlier this evening, a trying week.'

'It doesn't matter,' she returned guardedly, seeking a sign of derision in his expression. There was none that she could detect and she relaxed, giving him a small smile. 'It's over now, and it's Saturday tomorrow so I can sleep late if I want to.'

He seemed about to say something else, then changed his mind. Giving her a nod, he turned towards the door, pulling his car-keys from his pocket. She hurried forward.

'I'd better see you out – so I can lock up again after you.'

Again that small nod, and he stood back to let her lead the way. Automatically, she walked silently, trying to be as quiet as possible when she opened the glass door to the outer hall.

Mrs. Saunders was nervous about security and besides the normal lock on the door there were two large bolts on the heavy front door. Miranda drew the bottom one, but the top one was stiff and a shade too high and for her to reach easily. After a moment or so of watching her wrestle with it J.S. touched her shoulder and motioned her to stand aside.

'Let me,' he said.

The bolt gave, with a screech that set Miranda's teeth on edge. 'Hasn't she heard of the silent deterrent?' J.S. said in a whisper, and Miranda felt an uncontrollable desire to giggle.

It bubbled from her as she fumbled for the Yale catch and tugged the door open. She sensed that J.S. was grinning too, and she turned to see, only to freeze as the sound of a door slamming reverberated through the silent house.

'Who's there?'

The thin, alarmed cry came from the stairhead.

Miranda looked up and dismay widened her eyes. Mrs. Saunders stood up there, clutching a pink candlewick dressing gown round herself with one hand and hanging on to the banister rail with the other.

Jason Steele muttered, 'Here we go!' under his breath and pushed the door shut again on the rain-laden wind that was sweeping in.

Miranda said quickly, 'It's all right, Mrs. Saunders. It's just me.'

'You . . .?' Mrs. Saunders moved slowly down two stairs, bending forward uncertainly. 'But how did you get in? I locked up myself and—'

'No— We – that is, Mr. Steele is just going. I'm sorry to disturb you, but we—'

'Just going?' Mrs. Saunders was taking in the tall male figure standing in the shadows behind Miranda, and a very different expression was darkening her face. 'You mean you're not coming in? You mean that you and this – man have been—' She seemed to struggle for words. 'You were sneaking downstairs at this time of the morning? How dare you?' She advanced another step. 'I saw the strange car outside when I came home, but I never—'

'No! Wait!' Miranda started forward, incredulity rushing

52

over her as she realized just what was the conclusion Mrs. Saunders had jumped to. 'Listen, it's all right, Mrs. Saunders, I can explain. Mr. Steele is my boss, of Carona-Steele. He brought me home, and he's just got back from—'

'I don't care who he is or where he's come from,' Mrs. Saunders broke in. She was descending the rest of the stairs now, all trace of her former alarm gone, leaving her face grim with anger. 'Whatever he is to you is no business of mine,' she grated, 'or what you are to him, but I'd prefer it kept out of *my* house. And don't try to tell me it's business at this time of the night.' She drew a deep aggrieved breath and rushed on: 'Oh, they warned me what I was risking if I let strangers into my house, and I didn't believe them. I'm shocked and disappointed in you, Miss Meake. I thought you were a decent, quiet girl, and after the tale you told me about where you used to live, and the way your aunt brought you up, I felt sorry for you. Well,' her mouth tightened, 'I won't be taken in again, that's for sure, nor will I stand for any more of this sort of thing. Men coming and going from *my* house at all hours of the night. It isn't right!'

'Mrs. Saunders!' Miranda fell back, shocked by the tirade. 'You – you're quite mistaken. I can explain, if only you'll—'

'I don't think it's necessary,' Mrs. Saunders interrupted. 'As I said, it's no business of mine. But I'll have to ask you to leave, I'm afraid. I have Jean to think of, you know, and it just won't be suitable.' She turned away, looking fixedly at the stairs. 'You'd better make other arrangements as soon as you can.'

Miranda gasped. All the colour had drained from her cheeks, and a sick fear tightened in her stomach. Her flat. Her lovely little flat. It couldn't be true! She had to make Mrs. Saunders listen, make her understand. She started to speak, and felt Jason's hand grip her arm.

'Just a moment, Mrs. Saunders,' he said quietly.

The angry woman turned, almost unwillingly.

'Your imputations are not only unpleasant,' he said clearly, 'they are unfair, and they are also unfounded. However, I assure you I shall certainly see that Miss Meake *does* leave. After this I would not allow her to stay.'

'What!' Mrs. Saunders stared at him, and Miranda gasped. She looked up at him, more dismayed than ever by his unexpected interference, and then forgot what she was trying to say as his arm went round her shoulders and deliberately drew her close to his side. The protectiveness in the gesture rendered her speechless, and his next statement made her wonder if it were all a dream.

'Miss Meake is going to marry me,' he said in the same clear tones. 'If you've anything further to say you will address it to me.'

There was a moment of stunned silence. Miranda thought she had imagined it, then a wildness possessed her and she spun to face him, seeking confirmation that it was all a dream. But Jason's hard arm across her shoulders was no dream, nor was his crisp order:

'Don't argue, Miranda, and don't worry.'

'But – but I—'

'I'll see you tomorrow. We'll talk about it then.' Under the now startled gaze of Mrs. Saunders he coolly put one hand under Miranda's chin and tilted her face up. Quite deliberately he bent to her mouth and kissed her without hurry.

Then he gave her a gentle push and nodded in the direction of the stairs. 'It's time you got some sleep. Go on, Miranda.'

Unable to take her gaze from his face, she backed away to ascend the stairs like a sleepwalker.

Forgotten, as though she didn't exist, was the dumbfounded Mrs. Saunders.

CHAPTER FOUR

WHEN the sunrays stole through the chinks in the curtains next morning Miranda threw off the bedclothes and decided she must have dreamed it all.

The room seemed so utterly normal, the little bedside clock so steady and unhurried in its tick, and that undefinable lack of urgency that was so delightfully characteristic of non-working mornings was back after an absence of five days. In all, it was the dawn of another Saturday, a dawn looked forward to all week.

She sat up, her bare toes fumbling around by the bedside for her slippers, and began to assess in the cool light of day the odd events which had been no dream. Hadn't she lain awake most of the night, or what was left of it, wondering whatever had possess J.S. to make the most extraordinary statement she had ever heard from his lips? Her imagination had devised quite a number of reasons as it pondered the question during those wakeful hours. Some of them were plainly preposterous – she *had* once heard of a man who married a girl he hardly knew because he had to produce a wife in order to claim an unexpected inheritance, but J.S. didn't appear in such need of worldly goods that he'd have to resort to *that* length.

Others were equally fanciful, but of so tender and personal a nature she scorned herself for even admitting them – how could she imagine that J.S. was the type suddenly to discover an all-consuming passion for a girl he hardly knew, who was, to put it kindly, a shy, introspective and not very important member of the Accountancy Department staff? No, there was only one reason that stood up to prolonged logical study: J.S. had a peculiar and unpredictable sense of humour.

She got up, heedless that her toes had failed to locate the missing slippers, and pattered on bare feet to the window. She drew open the curtains and stared down at two sparrows flirting in the sooty shrubs beneath the plane tree, and a wistfulness shadowed her eyes. She thought she was beginning to know a little of the way J.S.'s mind worked.

He was so used to wielding authority it was now automatic; he possessed an undeniable streak of arrogance coupled with a strange, ruthless charm, and the combination of the three made it impossible for him to ignore any situation which presented a challenge or placed a difficulty in his path. So he dealt with it, and walked on.

The night she always thought of as 'that night' had been the first example of this that she had experienced; this was the second. And she had to admit that he had resolved an awkward situation last night. Perhaps it had been the first solution that came into his head, but it had certainly shaken Mrs. Saunders. *'To say nothing of what it did to me!'* she whispered aloud.

And it had really been her fault in the first place, she admitted wryly to herself. If she hadn't been so soft-hearted . . . After all, J.S. was tough and resilient – he wouldn't be where he was in the business world if he wasn't – and the lack of an hour or so's sleep in an armchair wasn't going to break him, even if he'd just flown in after a gruelling coast-to-coast tour of their American interests. She sighed. Despite this the incident brought an endearing little memory and she could not help remembering the hard lean lines softened in sleep, curiously young with an appeal that had made her want to touch and smooth the silver streaks at his temples . . .

Abruptly she turned away and snatched up her housecoat. She was being quite ridiculous. He'd probably be in hoots over it by now. He'd expect her to share the joke: one large joke instead of one spot of bother with a straitlaced landlady. The trouble was, she told herself miserably as she got into the bath, she would still have to leave the flat. Setting aside all his non-sense about not allowing her to stay there, she couldn't face telling the truth when the moment of explanation came. For even if Mrs. Saunders relented and said she could stay, Miranda couldn't bear to face her and confess that J.S.'s statement had simply been a quick and convenient way out of a troublous situation.

But he'd kissed her!

She retreated into the folds of the big towel and averted her gaze from her rosy reflection in the mirror. Last night she had been totally unprepared for his kiss, and when it came she had been so stiff with dismay at Mrs. Saunders's attack she hadn't felt a thing except the pressure of two warm lips on her own. But now . . .

A *frisson* of sheer delight coursed from head to toe every time she remembered that kiss . . .

'Miranda . . . ?'

She started almost guiltily at the urgent-sounding summons. Opening the door a few inches she met Mrs. Saunders's anxious eyes.

'I thought you must be in here – there's a phone call for you downstairs. Can you come down, or shall I . . .? I think it's your fiancé,' she added hurriedly, 'but he didn't give his name, just asked for you.'

'I'll come.' Miranda rushed past her, clutching her big towel round herself, and flew downstairs leaving a trail of white talcum footprints along the landing carpet. Her heart was thud-ding and she was breathless as she whispered into the phone: 'Yes – it's Miranda Meake here . . .'

'Good morning,' said J.S. in tones that betrayed nothing of an exhausting previous day. 'Any bother after I left last night?'

'No.' Her mouth went dry and she couldn't think of a single suitable contribution towards the conversation.

'Good. Now listen, Miranda,' he went on crisply, 'I'm in a rush today – the Chairman's cancelled his golf this morning, so

56

I can't possibly cancel *him*. And Wally Ambrose is joining us for lunch, which means an extended session. I doubt if I'll be free much before three. It may be later. What have you got on today?'

'A towel at the moment,' she said wildly.

'A what?'

But before she could speak he laughed softly. 'Did I get you out of the bath? It did occur to me I might get you out of bed, but I didn't think . . . Never mind, I won't keep you dripping there. I'll pick you up about seven. All right?'

She nodded, then realized the inanity of it and murmured a slightly more audible assent.

'Good,' he said. 'See you,' and rang off.

She put the phone down and turned slowly to see Mrs. Saunders hovering along the hall. The woman came along towards her, her expression uncertain.

'I didn't know you were engaged to him,' Mrs. Saunders said awkwardly. 'I wouldn't have been so hasty if I'd known. But I did get a bit of a fright when I heard you, so late . . .'

'Yes, I understand.' Miranda bit her lip as she read the sign of the olive branch in the older woman's anxious expression. Quickly she explained what had happened and this time there was no disbelief or interruption.

Mrs. Saunders nodded. 'I'm sorry I was abrupt, and of course you know you don't have to leave, until you have to – you'll be house-hunting now, I expect.'

She smiled, and Miranda started to edge away, murmuring an awkward response. Fortunately, Mrs. Saunders credited the awkwardness to a more obvious cause and made a shooing movement at her. 'Yes, go on,' she smiled, 'before you catch your death of cold standing in this draughty hall.'

Thankful for the chance of escape, Miranda seized it and fled. She could see all the friendly questions looming ahead. What kind of ring? What kind of a wedding? When . . .? And where? To say nothing of the friendly advice. Depression weighed on Miranda as she regained the privacy of her room. Common sense made her want to wish she'd never uttered that impulsive invitation last night, for think of the bothersome explanations she would have to make sooner or later, but some wayward part of her trembled with a half-fearful, half-joyous expectancy that made the long hours of the day seem strangely leaden . . .

57

She dithered too long over her choice of dress for the evening and his knock at the door came at exactly seven o'clock. There was no time to change her mind yet again and remove the lavender voile Juliet dress in favour of the more trendy polka-dot satin with the huge sleeves. Susan had been crazy about the blue and silver dotted frock that had cost far more than her budget really allowed, but she had a lingering doubt about whether it suited her as much as the softer flowing voile with its close-fitting bodice embroidered with silver. J.S. haunted the sophisticated night-spots; goodness knew where he planned to dine tonight, and she'd die if she let him down . . .

She hurried to open the door, and the moment of anxiety expired instead as she saw his encompassing glance and the kind of warm light in his eyes that can make a woman feel beautiful.

She flashed him a smile that held unconscious appeal and said shyly: 'I'll just get my wrap . . .'

Her heart was beating tensely as she went downstairs and got into the car. He had said little beyond a conventional greeting, and she wondered if she were imagining an air of restraint about him, one she had not formerly noticed in his manner. He drove away, and all at once her spirits plummeted into dejection. It was silly getting excited, as though it were a special date; silly even bothering to take her out just to laugh over that stupid excuse last night . . . She turned suddenly, ready to blurt out all her thoughts, and his intent profile wavered towards her for an instant before he returned his attention to driving.

'I'm feeling remiss,' he said, before she could speak, 'you look so charming I should have booked a table somewhere where I could show you off.'

The compliment took her off balance and made her lips part with pleasure. The flagging spirits promptly soared again and she wondered if he intended taking her back to that Hadean cavern where the lighting effects could turn the most ordinary apparel into the unusual and the unusual into the extraordinary . . . 'Yes, the Rotunda is a bit dim and smouldery, isn't it?' she ventured.

'I'm not taking you to Charlie's' he said coolly, and touched a switch along the dash. Music came from the radio, and he lapsed into a silence without divulging anything further concerning his plans for the evening.

But for the moment it didn't matter; she felt quite content to relax back in the luxurious car and watch the cavalcade of the city lights flash by. It did not seem very long before he swung the car into a quiet residential avenue and she caught a glimpse of a black and white sign on tall dignified iron railings. She thought it said Byrne Square, then she forgot it as they stopped outside a tall Georgian house with six steps leading up to its imposing panelled door.

J.S. got out, walked round the front of the car to open the passenger door, and held out an escorting hand. 'I thought we'd dine at home tonight,' he said easily. 'We'll be able to relax and talk more easily.'

His home! She faltered, looking up at the dark façade of the house, uncertain what to say to this and more uncertain of those dark-curtained enigmatic windows which gave no hint of what lay behind them; Jason Steele's house.

Before she could respond the door opened and a woman stood outlined against the oblong of amber light. She was quiet and pleasant-faced, and Miranda's heart gave an unwarranted bump of relief as she heard the woman say, 'Good evening, Mr. Steele,' and saw that her neat blue belted dress was actually a well-cut overall.

'About ten minutes or so, Libby,' he said, turning to slip Miranda's wrap from her shoulders.

Libby nodded, taking the wrap from him.

He opened a door to the left of the long hall and motioned Miranda to enter. She found herself in a warm, booklined room with scarlet and blue Turkey carpeting and dark leather buttoned armchairs. A desk stood near the tall window and on it stood a silver tray with crystal glasses and tantalus.

It was not the kind of room she had pictured him in, or rather, it was not what she would have expected to find. If she'd defined her imagined picture of his personal background she would have expected something like the striking white and burgundy scheme of his office suite, not this decidedly old-fashioned study. There was a portrait above the fireplace, in oils and heavy gilt frame, of a strong-featured man, who, despite the stiff wing collar and sombre black Edwardian tailoring, was so like Jason in features as to be quite startling.

'My grandfather,' said Jason, following the direction of her glance. 'My father wouldn't have him in the boardroom! The portrait,' he added, seeing her eyes widen. 'He was a tyrant.'

She thought better of remarking on the resemblance and failed to see Jason's mouth twitch. 'Martini or sherry?' he asked.

'Sherry, please.' She stayed near the fireside, the ball of tension beginning to reform inside her. A disturbing thought had suddenly occurred, bringing instant conviction that she had been rather foolish. Surely she had read far too much into two of his recent statements. Last night he had said, 'We'll talk about it tomorrow,' and this morning, 'I'll pick you up at seven.' And she'd dressed for a special occasion ... But he'd said nothing about taking her out to dinner – hadn't he just remarked in the car? 'I should have booked a table somewhere ...'

Miranda's heart sank. She'd taken too much for granted. Probably he had just intended to take her for a drink, for half an hour or so, long enough to dismiss the silly engagement nonsense and have a giggle over it, and then he'd found her dressed to go on the town ...

'If you want me to drink it for you, say so.'

She started. He was standing in front of her, holding out the glass of sherry, and something in the sardonic grey eyes made her colour up. The rim of topaz in the cut crystal was perfectly motionless, but as she took the glass his warm fingers encountered her own and the rim of topaz shimmered and tilted violently in her unsteady hand.

'You look as though you've just discovered a painful truth,' he said softly.

She turned away. 'Perhaps I have.'

'If you prefer something else you don't have to drink that,' he said in the same soft tone.

'It's a beautiful sherry,' she returned carefully.

He rested one arm along the pale green marble mantelpiece and regarded her from under half-closed lids. 'You're wishing I hadn't made that somewhat presumptuous announcement last night, aren't you? And you're afraid to say so.'

It was doubtful if any question could have been more calculated to throw her into confusion than this one. Pride screamed its affirmative that would answer the first and refute the sting in the tail, but the hurt wouldn't be denied, nor the anger that he could treat it all so coolly. It took an effort to appear outwardly calm, but she thought she succeeded as she moved a pace away and pretended to study a beautifully carved ivory figurine in the high-domed alcove at the side of the fireplace.

'It might have saved a lot of trouble if you hadn't,' she said flatly.

'What kind of trouble?' He had not moved.

'Well . . .' her shoulders lifted with a wry little gesture, 'isn't it obvious?'

'No, and I'm not anticipating any difficulty in dealing with any trouble that might materialize.'

Her mouth compressed at the unconscious arrogance of this statement. 'I don't doubt it, Mr. Steele, but as you have so little understanding it would be rather pointless my trying to explain.'

'Oh, Miranda!' There was pretended shock in his voice. 'No understanding? I did try to help. After all, I got the impression that your reputation was at stake. Or is that another old-fashioned idea these days? Don't girls care about their reputations any more?'

'Of course they do!' She spun round to face him and her eyes sparkled stormily. 'And it's not funny! But it would have been better if you'd left me to deal with it in my own way, instead of – of the way you did, and making me look ridiculous.'

'I never thought it was funny.' There was a changed note in his voice, and a distinct acidity as he added: 'The way I see it, the only rather ridiculous person is the worthy Mrs. Saunders.'

He put his hands on her shoulder and an enigmatic smile touched his mouth as he looked down into her widening eyes.

'But it was natural that she should make a fuss.' Miranda sighed and shook her head, her brief spurt of anger already subsiding. Jason's world and that of Mrs. Saunders were as far apart as two planets, and it was impossible to make him understand the kind of interest she would face and the embarrassment of finally ending it. 'After all, it's her house and I'm still a comparative stranger.'

'No, the woman's an idiot to jump to the conclusion she did,' Jason said forcefully. 'One look at you should have been enough.'

She stared up at him, conscious of the warmth of his hands and the sudden silence of the room enclosing them in a suddenly disturbing intimacy. His mouth curved again.

'I think you're nearly as innocent as Mrs. Saunders,' he said softly. 'She's forgotten, a long time since.'

'I don't understand.' She looked down, her heart beginning to beat quickly, almost as though it bucked at danger.

'I know you don't. Mrs. Saunders has forgotten, and you have yet to make the first memory.' Imperceptibly he was drawing her closer and willing her to meet his gaze. 'Mrs. Saunders thought we'd been making love. But doesn't she remember that lovemaking leaves certain delightful tell-tales in a girl's eyes? And a glow to illuminate them?' He bent his head till his mouth barely brushed her temple. 'I'm afraid you didn't have that glow, Miranda. Only a guilt without even a worthy sin to justify it.'

A sigh shuddered through her and she caught desperately at senses that wanted to desert her. The warmth of his breath stirring the tendrils at her temple, and an increasing awareness of his masculine strength brought an overwhelming desire to offer provocation. If she were to turn her head just enough to ... so that he could take her lips if he wanted to ...

She almost gasped aloud as the discreet tap came at the door. Jason's grasp slackened but did not release her while he called an acknowledgment to the housekeeper's reminder that dinner was ready.

He smiled, then stepped back and picked up the glass of sherry she'd scarcely touched. 'It's time to eat – and you haven't finished your sherry.'

Wordlessly she took it, and wondered if she had imagined relief in his voice when that summons had come from Libby ...

*   *   *

During the meal that followed he kept the conversation to completely impersonal topics. Libby served a faultlessly cooked meal with a quiet, unobtrusive skill that evoked secret admiration in Miranda. She wondered how many unseen staff the house held, or if Libby were the only one. Somehow she had the impression that Jason would dislike too many people around him in his home in the spells he spent there – he was away so often, more of his time would be spent in the impersonal atmosphere of hotels than in the privacy of his own home.

By the time dessert was finished she had discovered that Jason was knowledgeable about art and collected oriental pieces, jade and ivory in particular; that he had a catholic taste in music but professed himself no expert personally at any aspect of it – there was a Steinway in the lounge which he referred to as an ancient family status symbol and tendered to her a casual invitation to try it, obviously remembering her earlier confidences concerning herself – and lastly that he was on the governing board of a children's home in the Midlands.

'And please don't say "pity the poor orphans!"' he concluded.

'I wasn't going to.' She felt surprise at this divulgence; it was an unexpected personal glimpse into the man behind the tycoon, and an orphanage was the last thing she would have thought of in connection with the high-powered, undeniably arrogant J.S.

'Is it in a town or out in the country?' she asked, after a brief pause while he refilled her wine glass.

'It's about five miles out of Milborough, in an old manor house. About a dozen of the older boys live at the manor farm.'

'Do you go there very often?'

He tilted the wine in his glass and shook his head. 'I wish I could spare more time, but it's impossible, I'm afraid.'

'So you don't have much chance of getting to know the children,' she mused.

Rather abruptly he drained his glass. 'I don't have time to sentimentalize about individual children, if that's what you mean. Such time as I do have to spare is devoted to the more mundane matters connected with the financial side of the home.' He tossed his napkin on to his side plate and she received the impression that he regretted introducing the subject. 'Libby will have taken the coffee into the lounge . . . shall we go through?'

Without speaking, she rose. His hard statement had made plain his views on sentiment and she still felt the sting of recoil from his words. The feeling served to stiffen her guard against him and the increasing attraction she knew she could not deny he held for her. As he showed her to the other room she made a sudden resolve to try to keep out of his way in future. Not that it was likely to be very difficult – his path lay along a very divergent route from her own – and after tonight it was extremely unlikely that fate would throw another set of circumstances like those which had led to her presence here tonight. Which was just as well. In moments of cold sanity she saw all the danger signals that a fast-beating heart, a certain tensity, and that driving compulsion to be near one particular man

63

meant. It would be folly to let herself fall for Jason Steele, of all men ...

That her resolve had come too late did not occur to her as she assumed her frail mantle of defence and held her head with an air of cool aloofness when she entered the door he indicated. She stepped into the long spacious room that ran from front to back of one whole side of the ground floor, and fell in love with it instantly.

The walls were pale primrose, the paintwork white, and warm browns and ambers predominated in the soft furnishings. A thick, honey-hued carpet stretched from wall to wall, with a big oval Chinese rug of silky green and gold in the centre, and the whole was illuminated by diffused lighting from wide opaque panels in the ceiling. It was the kind of room that created an instant illusion of warmth and welcome as well as luxurious comfort, and Miranda's cold resolve melted as she sank into the deep cream cushions of one of the armchairs.

Libby came in then with the coffee tray. She smiled at Miranda and set the tray on a long low table of glass and delicately wrought curly white metal. She went out, and Jason dropped into a chair, crossing his long legs and lounging back with one arm crooked behind his head. He waved at the tray. 'Go on – that's one job my feminine guests always have to do. I like mine black. No sugar.'

'I remember.' She sat forward and reached to the tray. Her interest was still caught by the wealth of discovery the room held for new visitors. Here was part or all of his collection of jade and ivory, not housed in museum-like cabinets as were some collections but spaced out in modern wall units of glass and white and in harmony with the room. One item in particular stood out, an intricately carved pagoda some eighteen inches high which stood on a small table near where she was sitting. It evoked in her that strange fascination the East inspires so readily.

'Coffee first,' said Jason, following her glance, then added with some satisfaction, 'It never fails.'

She concentrated on holding the silver coffee pot very steady. 'You mean everyone admires the ivory pagoda?'

A rather wicked grin touched his mouth. 'It's one of my lures. I have several placed at strategic points around the room.'

'Really?' Gravely she handed him his coffee. 'Do you need lures, Mr. Steele?'

'Who doesn't — at least once in a lifetime?' A quirk of the dark brows had replaced the grin. 'I find the Chinese boxes within boxes are the most irresistible.' He reached out lazily to point. 'Those.'

She had heard of this particular miracle of oriental craftsmanship, but this was the first opportunity she had had of examining one closely. However, she contented herself with a glance and resisted the temptation to accept the unspoken invitation to get up and cross to the small table behind his chair where the ivory box stood. Instead, when he seemed to have left the conversational ball in her court, she remembered a small question that had caused her some puzzlement.

'How did you know I'd moved, Mr. Steele?' she asked.

'Moved?'

His frown of query was quite genuine, and she gestured. 'That afternoon you sent for me. Because I hadn't told Records.'

'Oh, that . . . I wanted to get in touch with you. Someone called Miss Vanda Vayle informed me over the phone that you didn't live there any more.'

For a moment of astonishment she wondered why he had made such a fuss. When she was in the same building seven hours a day, five days a week . . .

'Was it something important?' The tension was building again, making her voice stiff.

'I forget now.' The words sounded light, but there was a calculated undertone to them that deliberately tantalized. 'Maybe I wanted to send you that hotel bill.'

'But that was after I offered you—!' She stopped abruptly, her mouth setting as she met the dark glints of amusement in his eyes. She indicated the coffee-pot. 'Do you want any more coffee?'

'Please.'

He held out the empty cup and she had no option but to go to him. Evading his eyes, she took the cup and saucer, but as she turned away he reached out and caught her free hand. Gently but insistently he tugged, and the pressure brought her helplessly off balance. The cup rocked on the saucer, and the involuntary movement she made to steady herself brought her against his legs. A tremor shot through her as the hard warmth of his thigh burned into her own.

She said unevenly, 'Don't you want that coffee, after all?'

'Not really.'

She looked down into the age-old challenge in a man's eyes and met it with difficulty. 'Then do you mind if I finish mine?'

'You're my guest!' With the mocking little statement he released her, and trembling unsteadily she put the length of the glass table between herself and temptation. From beneath lazy lids he watched her refill her cup and then sip it as though the action were the most vital one of the moment. When she had finished he observed carelessly:

'So I can take it that you don't want to marry me, after all?'

With a sense of shock she realized she was still trembling inwardly and that flare of wantonness he had aroused in her earlier that evening was far from subdued. Its potency both frightened and shamed her, and she sought desperately to counteract its effect by clinging to her resolve and matching his carelessness with flippancy.

'I don't think we need carry the farce that far. It was a clever move and did the trick, so,' she forced a brilliant smile, 'I won't try to keep you on the hook, Mr. Steele.'

His brows flickered. 'I wasn't aware I was on the hook – I learned to avoid the delicate bait a long time ago, little Miss Meake.'

Already her brief spurt of defiance was spent. She looked away. 'I – I didn't exactly mean that. It was just – well, one of those silly things that happen when—' she shrugged awkwardly, not knowing how to say that it seemed stupid to drag out the silliness to this extent, even if it did seem to amuse him.

'I don't think you're quite sure yet what you *do* mean.' He uncoiled like a lithe spring out of his chair. 'I think perhaps a little music may help. What would you like? Tom Jones or Stravinsky?'

She gave a gesture of hopelessness. and the sardonic little half smile played round his mouth as he crossed to the stereo set-up in the corner near the french window. He rifled through a section of the long record unit and selected one. A moment later the sensuous, pervading rhythm of a latin-American mood piece flowed into the room. The strings were sweet, an inviting refrain that lay like a sparkling foil on the low throbbing beat of drums not yet allowed to approach their climax of domination.

Jason moved, soft-footed, to touch switches, and the pearly radiance dimmed overhead, leaving soft pools of light from two crystal wall lamps. The room took on a new warmth, an enfolding intimacy to veil the tender trap with velvet.

The soft steps paused behind her chair, and her heartbeat vied with the throb of the music.

'It's known as setting the scene,' Jason said calmly.

'I realize that.' She took a deep breath. 'But I didn't come here for seduction.'

'I'm well aware of that.' He moved round and looked down into her wide eyes. Her cheeks had gone perceptibly paler, but there was determination in the tense line of her upturned face. He reached out and ran one questing forefinger down the taut little outline. 'I'm also aware that I've picked myself an apprehensive little nymph this time. And so . . .' He left his sentence unfinished and turned away, opening a polished ebony box and extracting a cigarette from it. Flame leapt from the onyx lighter and snapped out again before he swung back to face her.

'Contrary to whatever you may have heard about me,' he went on calmly, 'I don't make a practice of seducing unwilling victims. And so . . . it's been a delightful evening, and the moment you make for that door I shall understand it's time to take you home.'

The thin blue coils of smoke spiralled up steadily from the glowing tip and Miranda stared aghast at the lean mocking face behind it. His expression flickered into a slight frown and he added abruptly: 'I'm sorry, I didn't offer you . . . Forgive me.'

'No,' she put out a refusing hand, as he indicated the cigarette, 'I don't.'

'Wise girl – I give up each morning and start again each night,' he said lightly, as though to the most casual of acquaintances.

'That's better than the other way around,' she said in a voice that didn't seem to belong to her.

'The other way around? Oh yes! I see. But I do cheat with the occasional cigar during the day.'

She smiled mirthlessly. 'It's very difficult, isn't it, to give up bad habits one enjoys. I think perhaps it's time I – I—' She bit her lip and forced her limbs to move towards the door.

'Yes, of course.' Unhurriedly he sought an ashtray and care-

fully stubbed out the half smoked cigarette. 'I'll see you home.'
He straightened. 'There's just one other thing.'

Almost at the door, she stopped.

'I did mean it, you know.'

Her lips parted, but made no sound.

He looked at her steadily. 'I do mean to marry you.'

CHAPTER FIVE

SHE had no idea how many seconds ticked by while she stood
there with Jason's proposal echoing through her mind. The
seconds could have been hours, so timeless did the spell of
silence seem, until Jason himself broke it by saying coolly:

'I think you need a drink before you commit yourself.'

She became aware of the music still playing in the background and some part of her subconscious mused that it seemed
a very long recording. She saw him move to the cocktail cabinet, then the chaotic rush started to whirl in her brain.

J.S. wanted to marry her!

But she hardly knew him. He hardly knew her. Yet he'd said
it. It hadn't been her imagination. How could love come so
quickly? Had it come to him the way it had come to herself?
For she knew in a sudden delirious soar of joy that she had
fallen totally, utterly in love with him, It was indescribable.
Like a shooting star, the spinning of a great silver turntable of
sound like triumphant bells. A new world belonging only to
herself and Jason. *Jason!* Not J.S. Not Mr. Steele. The real
man behind the figurehead she'd scarcely known.

Then he came and put the cold glass in her hand and the
magic stopped. It wasn't real. He looked exactly the same. He
didn't even have that challenging glint in his eye, that mocking
temptation that had beckoned her to flirt with him only
moments ago. Why wasn't she in his arms? Sharing the zany
ecstatic nonsense secrets lovers shared? Or so she'd always imagined . . . not this block inside her that wouldn't let her believe, let her take the first step towards him . . .

'Are you serious?' she faltered.

'Deadly.'

She put out an unsteady hand. 'But how can you . . .? What
am I supposed to say?'

68

'One of three answers. The only three. Yes. No. Or don't know.'

The matter-of-fact statement only increased her bewilderment. 'But we – we hardly know each other,' she countered weakly.

'That's easily remedied.' He smiled with mocking indulgence. 'What do you want to know about me, Miranda?'

She sighed despairingly, still striving to keep a sense of proportion before that unshakeable self-assurance of his. 'It isn't as easy as that, Mr. Steele. Sensible people don't—'

'Let's leave out the vague generalities,' he broke in, 'and that silly little defence of yours. That is the last time you'll address me as Mr. Steele.'

'But you are—' She bit her lip, an hysterical desire to giggle suddenly overtaking her. 'I can't stop thinking of you as Mr. Steele. And *you* don't know me, not well enough to – to *marry* me.'

'That makes it more interesting.' He went to the stereogram and switched it off. 'Don't you want to get married?'

'Yes, of course, but . . .'

'And a home of your own?'

She nodded, looking down.'

'And children?

'I don't visualize a marriage without them,' she said in a low voice.

'You're going to need a man, then,' he said dryly.

'Yes.' She put her glass down and looked at him steadily. 'But I want love, and a permanent relationship.'

'Yes, I thought so.' He straightened and for a moment his eyes were remote, staring beyond her. 'I'll be honest, Miranda. I think that the old accepted idea of one permanent, idealistic relationship between a man and a woman is doomed to extinction, sooner or later. For how can anyone pledge their entire life and future to one person? It's impossible to tell what the next twenty-four hours will bring, let alone the next twenty-four years.'

'But that's the very reason why one must try. Don't you see?' she entreated. 'Because of that you have to try to make something that will endure. Something to hold to when everything else seems to disintegrate.'

'And so we come down to old basics. The love and the trust.' He held out one hand, and despite herself she took a step towards him. 'Have you any particular reason for not trusting me?' he asked softly.

She held his glance a moment, then looked down.

He watched the almost imperceptible shake of her head, then put his hands on her shoulders. A tremor ran through them under his touch, and his grasp tightened. 'I think you're more than half in love with me already,' he murmured, 'but you won't admit it.'

The cool assumption stung, and a choking lump rose in her throat. She pulled herself away. 'No! And I'm not going to admit it. Nor can I marry you. You must know it couldn't work, not between two people who scarcely know one another. I – I don't know why you're going on about it,' she finished raggedly.

'Because I want you,' he said flatly.

'You *want* me?' She spun round to stare at him. 'You mean you just want—?'

'I mean I want you, and I'm prepared to marry you.'

'Just like that! Without love?'

Disillusion was darkening her wide eyes, making them look enormous in her small pale face. He held up one hand.

'Forget about marriage for the moment,' he said calmly. 'Tell me, would you be prepared to have an affair with me?'

'No!'

'Why not?'

'Why not!' she echoed scornfully. 'Just like that! Have you any idea of how cold-blooded that sounds?'

'No.' His brows went up. 'Premeditated, I'll admit. But not cold-blooded.'

A chill sickness was creeping up round her heart. Despite the warmth of the room her hands felt icy, and she clasped them to still their trembling. 'I don't see any difference,' she said stubbornly. 'I don't want that kind of affair.'

'Are you afraid?'

There was a subtle change in his tone and a certain intenness in his eyes. Before that steady gaze her instinctive denial faltered. 'Yes,' she said flatly.

'Of me?'

'Of all the things a girl is afraid of.' She turned away. 'I shouldn't have to spell them out.'

'You've no need to be afraid. I'll take care of you, I promise.'

The intense silence that followed seemed to press round her, as though he bade it hold her prisoner until she gave him her answer. Her lips felt stiff, drained of their lifeblood, and it took every ounce of control to keep her voice steady as she said quietly: 'I'm sure you're quite sincere, but can't you see that you're making it sound more and more impossible? You – you might as well itemize it, like – like an order form. You want me, so you'll take care of me.' Her voice sharpened. 'Do you think you can buy me?'

'I said nothing about buying. Or giving. Whichever way you look at it a love affair is a two-way affair, Miranda.'

'Love affair! You mean when you feel like it you'll take me to a show and then expect me to go to bed with you. There'll be the week-ends when you're not away, and the evenings when you feel bored and you pick up the phone. Or do you expect me to move in here?' she cried wildly. 'And you'll take care of me. By which you mean money will take care of me!'

'What *do* you want from an affair?' he asked tautly.

'I've told you! I don't want an affair.' Her voice broke and her mouth trembled. 'Can't you see that what you suggest rules out everything that matters? Every tenderness, every trace of the unguarded, impulsive affection that should prompt a real love affair. There has to be mutual affection, and respect. You can't blueprint any relationship. Taking care of someone means protecting them. How can you protect them from the hurt *you* inflict yourself?'

She was shaking when she finished her impassioned outburst, and she did not hear his three quick strides that brought him to her side. When his hands seized her shoulders she started with shock and, too late, tried to evade his grasp.

'Oh no, you don't!' The first crack in his control showed in the fierce tightening of his fingers. They bit into the softness of her skin under the flimsy voile, making her flinch. 'You've said your piece,' he grated, 'now I'll say mine.'

Instinctively she put out her hands, but their lilac-tipped slenderness was as frail a defence as the flutter of butterfly wings against the tempest. Inexorably they were trapped against the ivory figured silk of his shirt as he pulled her against him.

'So you don't believe I can love, be impulsive, and invoke affection? You prefer to expect me to inflict pain? Look at me,' he commanded. His steely gaze bored down into her averted

71

face. 'Look at me!' he repeated.

Against her will, knowing deep down inside that if she obeyed she was lost, she raised her head and looked up into the dark, saturnine features.

'So you don't believe I can be tender,' he whispered mockingly.

She did not know the moment when the swift, imperceptible change had come, when the fierce grasp of iron fingers became a caress that stole and enfolded her within his arms; when the arrogant mouth became silent and feathered a long sensuous tracery of her brow, her temples, the oval curve of her cheek, and sought out the tender hollows of her throat as his arms curved and moulded her more closely than ever. Her bones felt as though they were turning to water, her limbs as though they would melt with the heat of ecstasy, and at last, when she murmured and felt she could not bear the longing an instant longer, his mouth took hers in a kiss that drew out the entire heart of her and made her, willing or not, the prisoner of his power.

Ageless moments later he drew back and looked down at her darkened eyes and the soft mouth that still quivered from his kiss. In his own eyes glowed a smouldering look strangely like triumph.

'Hello, Miranda Meake,' he whispered.

She could not speak, only give a tremulous sigh and bow her head. The little alarm bells of instinct were almost muffled now, but their weak message still strove to sound above the clamour of her senses and tell her she must regain control, do something about a situation fast becoming out of hand. But what . . .? She'd never known a man like Jason Steele; nor had she ever dreamed of the effect he could have on her if he chose to wield the charm of experience . . .

'I – I think I'd better go,' she said in a tiny strangled voice that sounded miles from her own ears.

He cupped one hand behind her head, pressing hard fingers under the disarray of her hair, and drew her flushed face into his shoulder.

'I think you'd better marry me, after all,' he said softly.

*　　　*　　　*

'Where do you want to go for our honeymoon?' he asked, three evenings later.

'I don't know.' She stared at the shimmer of lights reflected on the river and wondered when she would wake from the be-mused state she'd been in ever since the evening of Jason's proposal. *Jason!* She was going to *marry* Jason Steele. In three weeks' time. And for the time being it was still a secret. Jason's wish, this, but one she was quite happy to share, simply because it was his desire that it should be so. Although how she had managed to keep from crying it to the world she did not know; perhaps it was the somewhat daunting little reminder he had made as he drove her home that unforgettable evening: '*I hope you're prepared for the barrage you'll have to face when the news breaks at the office.*'

She had stared at him, at the sardonic curl of his mouth, her expression uncomprehending, for the office was as far from her mind at that moment as the moon, and he had added impatiently: 'It's plain to see that you haven't worked in a large concern for long. Chatter for the vicarage will have nothing on our grape exchange. Not that it worries me much, but there'll be no mercy for you – apart from not sparing your blushes.'

Instantly Rena Harvey had come into her mind, and she realized what Jason had foreseen. It did not need much stretch of the imagination to envisage the reaction when the news was known. Nor would Jason be quite as remote in his director's suite as one might imagine . . . She had wanted to tease him suddenly, tell him he was scared of the tales they might tell her about his past, but something in his expression stifled the daring little impulse and she had stayed silent, aware then as she was to be aware more than once in the future of how little she really knew him. And when she had walked into the building on the Monday morning, to the start-of-the week grouses and inquests on personal week-end affairs, it suddenly seemed better to agree with Jason's suggestion . . .

She became aware of Jason repeating his question:

'Where've you most wanted to go all your life?'

A breeze ruffled the surface of the water, breaking the bright garlands of lights into shimmering eddies. Her glance shifted and came to rest on Jason's well-shaped hand as it toyed idly round the stem of his glass.

'Acapulco,' she said instinctively.

The long fingers ceased their motion. His brows came together. 'Acapulco?'

The moment she spoke she had realized the inanity of her response. She shook her head. 'No – I didn't mean that. Forget

73

it, please. I – I was just being silly.'

'What made you say it?'

'I don't know.' She avoided his gaze and cradled both hands round her glass, raising it to sip before she said carefully: 'I don't mind where we go, as long as the sun shines.'

His mouth pursed. 'Well, it shines fairly consistently over there. Why not? I'll make the reservations tomorrow.'

With a feeling of increasing dismay she met his nonchalant regard and could not help exclaiming: 'But you said you could only take a week. It'll take a day to get there and a day to come back. We can't go all that distance for only four days!'

'Why not? I've gone farther afield for much less.'

She thought of the reason which had prompted her rash suggestion and wondered if he too were remembering the same occasion. 'It'll cost the earth,' she said weakly. 'I mean, when it's for business purposes you're forced to travel long distances, but not when we have the choice ... And it'll be appallingly expensive,' she added with a worried sigh.

He shrugged. 'It's a special occason, isn't it? Or is that a thing of the past now?'

'Of course not!' The shock in her voice made it clear that she still considered a girl's wedding day to be a very special day in her life. 'But I don't want you to think I'm unreasonable just because I made a stupid reply to a serious question. I mean, when you've so little time,' she hurried on, colouring under the cool scrutiny of his eyes. 'I'd be quite happy to stay here, a few days at the coast ... Devon or Cornwall ... or we could wait until you're not so tied up ... postpone the wedding until your holidays,' she ended rather wildly.

'I haven't had a conventional holiday for two years,' he said. He leaned forward, resting his elbows on the table and making steeples with his fingertips. 'I'm going to tick you off, Miranda, in this order: First of all, I do think you're a very unreasonable girl – but not because you want to go to Acapulco of all places for your honeymoon.' He paused for a moment, his expression enigmatic, giving her no clue as to how she was to take that definite statement, before he went on: 'Secondly, *I* wouldn't be happy with a few days in Devon or Cornwall. I'd prefer to be out of reach of the phone for a few days. They'd think twice before they dragged me back across the Atlantic, but anywhere in this country ... no, it's too handy. Thirdly, the answer's decidedly negative. I've always hated waiting for anything I

74

wanted,' he ended coolly.

She bit her lip and looked down. Behind the brusque practicality of him there was no pretence. He'd made no secret of his desire for her, and she would not have been woman if the knowledge of this did not start her senses hammering with pleasure and satisfaction. Of all the girls he could have had he had chosen her, had asked her to marry him.

Already she was closing her mind to that other alternative; that she go to him on his own terms. She was also closing her mind to speculation on what the outcome might have been had he chosen to exert a certain potent kind of persuasion instead of making that unexpected capitulation of a proposal of marriage. For the present it was enough to be in that wild, wonderful state of love that made it easy to answer all doubts to her own satisfaction. So what if her first attraction for Jason had been that of her own slender, physical self? Didn't everyone admit now that sheer physical chemistry was the mainspring? It came first, drawing two people together; until that certain attraction sparked there was little desire to explore one another's personalities, to discover those more subtle depths which people did not display to the casual world. The togetherness came later, she decided, and she had to remember that Jason was used to meeting masses of people. The world of commerce had made him hard and unsentimental. It would take a long time before Jason would drop that hard façade and betray the real man underneath.

'Have you told anyone?' he asked.

'No, not even Susan.' She smiled across the lamplit table. 'We did decide not to breathe a word until you got back from the Moscow trip, you know.'

He nodded. 'You're sure about the wedding plans? By next week it'll be too late to change your mind.'

'I'm sure,' she said firmly, knowing he was referring to their decision to have a very quiet wedding.

If she had had parents and a lot of relations it might have been different. In view of this it was easy to see the truth of Jason's objection to a large and lavish wedding; not because of the obvious expense but because he knew so many people it would be difficult to know when to draw the line under the invitation list. It would end up with half of London there. Coping with it all would become a burden rather than a pleasure, especially as Jason wouldn't get back from Moscow until four days before the wedding and Miranda would have to cope by herself. She would finish up as so many brides did after the last week of hectic pre-wedding rush – so tense and exhausted she'd be on the borderline of tears and hyteria. And all those scores of people she didn't know, total strangers ... yes, Jason was being sensible, small, quiet ceremony, no more than half a dozen close friends, a brief celebration, just a buffet and toast and cake at Jason's house, no more than half an hour before they left for the airport, and the guests could drink themselves silly to their hearts' content afterwards if they so wished ...

The secrecy proved easier to maintain than she had thought. The bug was still wreaking havoc among the staff and the returning victims were too full of their personal experience and sage advice to those on the point of succumbing to notice Miranda's suppressed air of excitement. She was one of the few who escaped the infection and the sense of immunity helped to heighten the dreamlike quality of those next two weeks.

It was almost like living a double life. By day she went demurely about her work; at evening she entered the sophisticated pleasure world Jason took for granted. For Jason doors opened and crowds parted, head waiters hurried forward and doormen saluted, and all ways seemed to smooth out ahead of him. Some of this particular essence came from Jason himself in his escorting of his fiancée. He protected and cosseted her, almost as though he were determined to bewitch her with charm.

It was all very new and heady, and perhaps it was partly the cause of her failure to notice that despite the crowded social hours she met very few of Jason's friends during those exciting two weeks. Nor did she question the fact that he seemed curiously loath to accept invitations from those acquaintances he did encounter casually at theatre or restaurant while in company with Miranda.

'I'm hopelessly tied up all next week,' was invariably his reply, sweetened with a charming, rueful smile. 'Ask us again after the thirtieth – I'll be back from Moscow by then.'

'Not spying, I hope!' was the responding sally to this, from an auburn-haired nymph in white suède and gilt leather they'd bumped into – literally – in the crush bar.

'*Quiet!*' hissed Jason ferociously, and in the giggle that followed drew Miranda away from the openly curious survey of the russet-capped nymph.

76

A little while later Miranda ventured on an afterthought: 'You're not, though, are you, Jason?'

'Not what?'

'Involved in anything like that?'

'Like what?'

'Spying.'

He gave an incredulous exclamation, and she rushed on anxiously: 'I read somewhere that they do sometimes get businessmen to pass information, bona fide travellers like yourself who are actually important executives, and they usually only use them the once.'

For a moment he stared at her, then sheer satanic mirth glowed in his face. 'Remind me to show you the secrets of the trade some time. I've a transmitter in my heel, a miniature camera implanted in my left eyelid – every time I wink at a girl! – and a stiletto down each sock. All the blackmailing price I must pay for my past indiscretions.'

She did not smile. 'I wish you weren't going away, all the same.'

'So do I – I mustn't forget to pack a couple of sink plugs.'

Amid all this there was one other noticeable aspect which caused her a certain wry concern and quite a lot of soul-searching long after the spying nonsense was forgotten.

For some reason known best to himself, Jason made not the slightest attempt to make love to her during that dreamlike spell of their brief engagement. His salutations were impeccably conventional and quite without any trace of the passion she had sensed in him the night of his proposal. He did not seem to expect the small warm declaration of love she longed to make but was too shy to offer without the encouragement that did not come, although he was unfailingly generous in all material ways.

She was clear-sighted enough to recognize the possibility of his desiring to anticipate their marriage – Jason had never pretended to wear the mantle of a saint and he had been strictly honest in his approach when he first admitted his interest in her – but now it seemed that this particular moment of decision was not to be thrust upon her, after all. She was not sure whether to be sorry or thankful, and, sure of her understanding of Jason, found herself, searching for the reason behind his unexpected restraint. Could it be that he was so confident of his power to invoke responding desire in her that he was content now to wait for the completeness of true marriage; the traditional way she had been brought up to envisage?

At times she wished she could confide in Susan, but dared not in case her friend could not resist telling Ray.

Fortunately Susan was too intent on her own affair to notice the new glow about her friend.

'Ray's different, isn't he?' she said thoughtfully.

'He seems a more serious type,' Miranda agreed. 'I don't think he's the flirtatious kind.'

'No, I don't think he is.' Susan lapsed into silence for moment or so. 'Sometimes I've wondered if he really wants a steady girl or just a friend. Please don't laugh, but he's never kissed me once, and we've been out four times this week. You *are* laughing!' she accused.

'I'm not, honestly,' Miranda denied. 'You'll have to be patient. He's probably wondering what you'd do if he started kissing you. How's he to know whether you'll slosh him one or go all aloof?'

'But he should know me by now,' Susan wailed. 'Honestly, you never know where you are with men. Either they expect the whole works the minute they meet you or they go on as though there were a glass wall in the way. I mean, I want to feel I'm attractive to him.'

Miranda inclined her head without speaking, knowing exactly how Susan felt. Her problem wasn't really an enigma, for Ray was only a year older than Susan and still youthfully uncertain of feminine reactions. Not in the least like Jason. Jason was no stripling, and his knowledge of feminine reactions to himself far more comprehensive than any man's should be, she thought with a sigh. If only Susan knew, she reflected wryly. Jason, for reasons best known to himself, seemed to have forgotten how much a kiss meant to a girl in love. The last few evenings had ended with a kiss so chaste it was almost an afterthought. And it would be playing with fire to make any invitations . . . To think that she had worried . . .

She sighed again softly. There was little comfort or advice born of experience she could offer the lovelorn Susan, except confirmation of her grumble; men were the most unpredictable creatures ever, and Jason the most unpredictable of all.

CHAPTER SIX

THE evening of Jason's flight to Moscow marked the end of the dreamlike idyll those past weeks had seemed.

The pressure was on again, at least as far as Jason was concerned, and all he could spare her was half an hour in a wine bar before he hurried off for a last-minute conference with the chairman immediately before the actual flight.

He was tense and abstracted as they settled in an alcove with their drinks, more like the impersonal, hard-headed Jason she remembered before the night she sought sanctuary in his office, and she sensed in him an impatience to be gone. The air of business stayed as he reminded her of the wedding arrangements she would have to check in his absence, and as he told her she was to consult Miss Mayo should any unforeseen snags arise.

'But I thought we weren't going to tell anyone until you got back,' she exclaimed.

'Exempting my secretary, in whom I've complete trust,' he said flatly. 'She's essential to my routine— I should have thought that you'd have realized that by now. I've given her all the instructions this afternoon and she'll see to everything for next week. All you'll have to do is your own personal packing and the last-minute things like going to the hairdresser.'

'I see,' she said rather stiffly.

'Oh, and fixing up Susan to give you moral support,' he added dryly.

'I'm planning to arrange that with her this week-end.' Miranda decided to ignore the ironic little sting in the tail of his remark.

'Does she know?'

'Not yet. I simply asked her to keep the thirtieth free for me.'

'Well, don't be mysterious too long,' he enjoined, glancing at his watch. 'Give her fair warning so that she can get her new dress or whatever you want her to wear. And remember what I said about that.'

Miranda nodded, touched by his unexpected understanding and the implied generosity. But she had already made her plans regarding Susan's dress and foreseen the blow it might present to her friend's slender budget. Nevertheless, she felt the fresh surge of love for him melt away the stiffness his brusque mien had induced and it gave her courage to say impulsively: 'What time will you be out of the meeting?'

'Why?'

'I'll wait for you – then see you off at the airport.'

He drained his glass and pushed it away. 'I'd rather you didn't. I'll probably be rushing at the last minute.'

'It doesn't matter.' Something made her persist in spite of his obvious reluctance to agree to her request. 'It's worth it to me, even if it's only a few minutes.'

He stood up abruptly and flicked at a speck on his lapel. 'I hope you're not going to be a possessive wife,' he said.

A crispness in his tone made this remark fall short of the jocular, and the eagerness died from Miranda's face. Her parted lips closed, then tightened. 'There's a difference between caring and possessiveness,' she said in a voice that wasn't quite steady. 'I think I can recognize it, Jason.'

'You'll be one of the few women who can, at least in my experience.' He waited with scarcely concealed impatience while she gathered up her bag and magazine and slid along the banquette. The table was set too near for ease in escaping the otherwise intimate corner and she caught her knee against one of the unseen supports beneath, making her stumble. His hand came out to steady her. 'Why do girls always make for these nooks that are so difficult to extricate oneself from?'

'I don't know.' She sighed under her breath for the ache in her knee. 'Why do men always stand aside until we've got in, so that they can sit at the end?'

'So that we can get out easily to pay for the drinks.' He pushed open the door, his car keys already jingling in his hand. 'I'm sorry to rush you, but I'm going to be late.'

'It doesn't matter.' She sat stiffly in the car and stared straight ahead. It came to her that they had almost quarrelled. Not quite, but the atmosphere was there, the kind of culture on which the seeds of argument could flourish. The thought sent a chill through her and his remark about possessive wives began to repeat itself over and over in her brain. Was that how quarrels began between lovers? As easily as that?

The word 'lover' lingered and brought a tiny furrow to her brow. Despite the fact that she was to marry Jason it was still strange to think of him as her lover, even more difficult to believe they were on the brink of marriage.

I still don't know him! she whispered soundlessly. How could one love a man yet not know him? And yet it seemed as though she had known his features, his tall form, the way he moved and the sound of his voice for ever. She shook her head, and became aware of the car slowing down to a standstill a few yards from the junction of the main road and Willow Grove.

'Do you mind if I drop you here?' he said. 'It'll save me that one-way detour at the other end of your road.'

'Of course not.' She took a firmer grip on her bag, knowing she must get out of the car yet reluctant to make the move. 'I'll see you when you get back, then. Have a good trip.'

It didn't seem that he was going to make any move towards her, and after a brief glance at his shadowy face she reached for the door handle.

'Miranda . . .'

She turned back instantly.

'You understand by now that I have two lives; my personal life, and Carona-Steele?'

She stared at him through the shadows, the movement of her head almost afraid.

'I try to keep them apart, though it isn't easy, nor is it always possible – Carona-Steele is too demanding. Too demanding to allow the distraction of a woman.'

Her mouth felt stiff. 'You want to change your mind?'

'What about?' He sounded puzzled.

'About me.' She dared not look up and an ache was beginning to race through her body.

A muffled exclamation escaped him. His hand slid from the wheel. 'Listen to me. This is exactly what I'm getting at, Miranda. I made a certain observation a while ago, to which you took exception.'

'I didn't!'

'You did, if not in words then in the quality of your silence since that moment. You wanted to see me off at the airport, but in this case it's better if you don't. I'm travelling with another businessman whom I'm meeting there. You'd simply be standing around and there'd be no time for exchanges of sentiments.'

'You mean I'd be a distraction,' she said flatly.

'I wasn't going to say that,' he said in cool tones, 'and don't start putting words into my mouth. All I'm trying to point out is that there'll be many times when my work has to come first – and this is one of them. If only women would realize that and not persist endlessly . . .' He broke off with an impatient sigh and a gesture that struck chill into Miranda's heart. 'It would save a hell of a lot of trouble,' he added.

'You sound as though you speak from experience,' she whispered.

'I do.'

The flat response did nothing to take away the chill of despondency. She took a deep breath, trying to appear calm. 'You said you were late,' she reminded him.

'That's better.' With a typically male carelessness he shrugged mockingly, seeming to slough off the air of the small, and to Miranda, tense incident. 'I'll see you after Moscow – and don't look so forsaken! It'll be all right after The Day.'

A slight smile, another of those chaste kisses that left bewilderment and a sense of dissatisfaction, a laconic, 'Out you get,' and she was walking the short distance to Syrian Lane.

Her heart felt curiously leaden as she let herself into the silent flat, and she had the feeling she was beginning to wake from a dream. The doubts crowded in on her, no longer suppressible.

It'll be all right after The Day . . .

But would it? Did Jason take marriage as seriously as she did? His proposal had been as sudden as unexpected, and the reason for it no secret. He wanted her, she didn't doubt it, but was she being naïve and foolish to believe that he must have some love for her, to desire her so much he wanted marriage, and that time would bring them closer in understanding? She had not made any secret of her own feelings, yet Jason had been rather conservative about his own, as though he was quite satisfied now that the arrangements were all settled and she had accepted his ring.

She looked down at it; the central sapphire, her birthstone, in a cluster of diamonds. She dared not think what it had cost – the trays brought for her inspection in the jeweller's had given no hint of anything so unromantic as price. Jason had practically chosen this one, seeming to divine it was the one she liked best of all, but she had hesitated a long while, suspecting that it was frighteningly expensive. Then Jason had tired of indecision.

'That's the ring,' he had said briefly, and given her no chance to demur.

Slowly she drew it from her finger, and her eyes grew wistful. He must love her the way she secretly longed and hoped . . . It was just that she had to realize he wasn't a sentimental kind of man. He was accustomed to making firm decisions, to knowing what he wanted and getting it, and to people obeying him without question. Tonight had to be discounted. He faced a last-minute conference, a long flight and a packed agenda at the end of it, and there was always that certain tension about business trips behind the Curtain, in spite of his unconcerned attitude towards this one.

And so she stilled the doubts, even though she knew she was making allowances for him. But wasn't that part of what love was all about . . .?

*　　*　　*

She had expected the days to drag while he was away: somewhat to her surprise they flew.

That week-end she said good-bye to working days at Carona-Steele, ostensibly to begin her annual vacation but in reality for good. Nothing occurred to necessitate her consulting his secretary, and no summons or query came from that redoubtable personage, nor did any sudden surprise rumour ripple like wildfire through the building.

Yes, it had been sensible to defer to Jason's wisdom, Miranda decided. Nevertheless, she felt a sense of loss as she tidied out her desk drawer and transferred the few personal items it held into her bag. It would have been wonderful to announce her own momentous news and watch its reception. She would love to see Rena Harvey's face . . .

She had to content herself with telling Susan and Ray that evening, whose reaction helped to make up for the flatness of her departure from Carona-Steele. As she had feared, Susan betrayed aggrievedness once she had got over the three stages of incredulity, disbelief, and dawning conviction that her leg wasn't being pulled.

'You might have told me,' she cried indignantly. 'I wouldn't have breathed a word to a soul, you know that.'

'We decided it was the best way. Jason didn't want a lot of fuss.'

'Well! You and J.S. You know, now I think of it I've noticed

83

you going dreamy-eyed when he's around.' Susan pouted. 'And I thought we didn't have any secrets.'

Tactfully Miranda steered the discussion towards wedding fashion and Susan soon forgave her in the excitement of planning what she would wear.

Miranda had already decided on a semi-informal dress of ivory terylene voile with the currently fashionable very full sleeves and close-fitting Victorian style bodice. There was silver threadwork edging the neckline and scalloped wristbands, and afterwards she would be able to wear it for parties or special occasions. So the following morning they concentrated on Susan's dress, finally choosing a lovely shell pink silk that suited her delicate colouring perfectly. Afterwards they went back to Miranda's flat to meet Jean, newly arrived from Edinburgh to take up residence under Mrs. Saunders' maternal wing.

She was a sunny-natured girl, inclined to be on the boisterous side, and entered wholeheartedly into helping Miranda begin her final preparations for the great day.

Suddenly there seemed a host of last-minute items to shop for and things to do if she were not to have a mad last-minute rush. A gorgeous set of pale blue matching cases arrived on the Monday; dress case, two smaller cases, overnight bag, and a beautifully fitted beauty case, which Jason had ordered and forgotten to tell her about, and the following morning brought a heavenly bouquet with the card: 'See you soon,' which set Miranda alight with joy and Jean with curiosity to see him.

It was Jean who bounded up the stairs, two at a time that evening, to gasp breathlessly: 'Phone for you – a personal call – it must be *him*!'

'From Moscow!' Miranda squealed. 'It can't be!'

But it *was* Jason calling her from Moscow.

At first she could only stammer when the call was connected and she realized she was really talking to him. His voice waxed and waned, strangely unreal across sea and continent, yet unmistakably his. Her heart raced with pleasure and the joyous little affections bubbled on her lips. But there was no time for them. After the brief opening courtesy he spoke crisply and quickly, and when he finished Miranda's mouth drooped with disappointment. Something had cropped up unexpectedly.

He wasn't coming back tomorrow.

He had to break his journey to meet a business contact in

Prague. A new development made this essential and there was no way of postponing the commitment.

'But when . . .?' faltered Miranda, prepared for the worst.

'Friday. Late Friday, I'm afraid.' He sounded weary.

'But that's the day before . . .'

'As long as it isn't the day after,' he said dryly. 'Now don't worry. And don't come to meet every flight if you don't hear from me. Have an early night and get your beauty sleep.'

'But that means I won't see you until—'

The line crackled and his voice receded into the distance. She thought he said something about a cable, but the gist was lost in the overlay of static moments before the line crackled and went dead. A moment later the dialling tone buzzed and there was nothing she could do but replace the receiver.

Panic wasn't far away as all the awful 'mights' presented themselves. He might not get back in time! He might be delayed longer than he expected. The wedding might have to be postponed! *Cancelled!*

Jean offered soothing assurances that nothing of the kind would happen. Men like Jason hopped international flights like Miranda hopped on the Underground, she said firmly. He'd be back all right.

Miranda wished she could feel as confident. And even if he did it was going to make things awkward. They were leaving on the afternoon flight on the Saturday, and if Jason didn't land in before the early hours of Saturday morning he was going to end up flying half-way round the world in those two days, with a few hours' stopover in London to get married, she thought hysterically.

She fretted all through Wednesday, and on Thursday decided to telephone Miss Mayo. It was a little deflating, even if a relief, to hear that he had been in contact with the office and Miss Mayo was in full possession of his schedule. There was nothing to worry about; everything was under control.

'You'll be a nervous wreck by Saturday,' Jean told her sternly. 'Do you know what I think? I think we should go out for the day tomorrow. I know! Let's go to Brighton. How about it?'

Miranda shook her head. 'I can't. I'm going to the hairdresser in the afternoon. And I might miss the phone.'

'That phone!' Jean waved her hands and sent the standard lamp rocking. 'If this is what love does I hope I escape it a while longer.'

Later, Miranda wished with all her heart she'd taken Jean's impulsive advice. If they'd gone on that jaunt designed to cram full that day of nerve-racking tension she might not have been at home when Susan called. And Susan might have paused and pondered the wisdom of acting the tutelary herald.

But she didn't. Jean decided to go and look up long-lost relations at Willesden, and obviously found them, for she had not returned when Susan arrived shortly after eight that evening.

Miranda was pleased though surprised to see her, knowing that Susan did a baby-sitting job every other Friday and this was the booked one.

'Ray's there holding the fort – or rather the baby,' she explained, looking round the room, at the open suitcase on the bed, the beautiful ivory dress hanging under its transparent cover, and the new undies of cobwebby nylon lace laid over a chair back in readiness for when Miranda dressed the following morning. 'Where's Jean?' she asked.

Miranda told her, then added excitedly: 'Miss Mayo rang up this afternoon – he'll be back on the evening flight. About nine, she thinks, and he's going to ring me as soon as he gets home.' Miranda sighed happily. 'She was so sweet – you know how cool and off-putting she usually is – and she wished me happiness and said she'd arranged the cars, and Libby has everything laid on at Byrne Square, and my luggage would be collected at nine in the morning, and if there was anything at all she could do personally I had to ring her at her home tonight. She asked was I nervous, and if I was I should have a long luxurious soak and then sip a cup of hot milk in bed and read myself sleepy and forget about tomorrow. As if I could! But I—' She stopped as she noticed Susan's stiff, unsmiling expression. 'Susan – what on earth's the matter?'

'I – I—' Susan licked dry lips. Suddenly she looked as though she were going to weep.

Miranda stared, searching for an explanation and suddenly finding one. Dismay clouded her face. 'You haven't come to tell me you can't come tomorrow? Oh, Susan! You can't let me down! I'll—'

Susan gave a choked exclamation and swung round. 'Oh – I wish I hadn't come. I wish – how am I going to say it?'

'Say what?' Alarm flared in Miranda's eyes. She dropped the jacket she was folding and took a step forward. 'What? What do you have to say?'

Susan sank down on the end of the bed and avoided Miranda's apprehensive gaze. 'I wish Jean was here. Maybe I—' She gulped. 'You're going to hate me, but I have to tell you, in case it *is* true, and tomorrow will be too late.'

An icy hand clutched Miranda's heart and a certain name seared into her brain in letters of fire. Jason! It could only be Jason. 'What?' she almost screamed. 'Susan, *tell me!*'

'Well,' Susan took a deep breath, 'the news is out now – in the office. Naturally, everyone got a surprise and everyone's talking about it. Except Jim Grayson – you know big Jim, the maintenance man, who always pats you on the shoulder and calls you "Beautiful", even old Miss Bates who's as ugly as sin. But he said he wasn't really surprised because his mate, Tom – the security man, you know? – told him he'd seen you and J.S. leaving the building together one night ages after everybody had gone, but he kept his mouth shut because that's his job and anyway he doesn't hold with gossiping about other people's affairs.'

Susan paused again, and Miranda clenched her fists to stop herself shaking Susan.

'Well,' Susan went on, 'somebody asked: why all the secrecy? and Rena turned on me, wanting to know if I'd known all along and why hadn't I told her. I was a bit narked at the way she spoke to me and so I told her it was none of her business. And then—' Susan gulped and looked up unhappily at Miranda's shocked face.

She swallowed hard. 'I can't remember word for word everything she said, but she made me promise faithfully to talk some sense into you before it was too late. If I didn't she was going to come here to see you herself.'

'Here?' Miranda paled. Desperately she strove to be calm, to dismiss Susan's unhappy tale-bearing with the scorn it deserved. For didn't they all know Rena Harvey? 'Doesn't she know I'm getting married tomorrow? Does she think I'm interested in anything she has to tell me about Jason? Whatever it is I don't want to hear it. It's in the past now. I – I couldn't care less if he ran a harem or kept half a dozen mistresses.' Her voice wavered but she kept her control. 'I know Jason has had affairs. I think I'd be more worried if he hadn't – he's not a boy. I'm not going to listen to anything from that poisonous woman.'

'Oh, no,' Susan sighed, 'you don't understand. I know she talks, but she isn't as bad as that. Please listen, it isn't just silly things like you making the biggest mistake of your life and he'll break your heart, and all that kind of thing. She's really worried about you. You have to be told.'

The ice of fear paralysed Miranda again. The brave denials stilled on her white lips and she could only stare at Susan with the anguish of entreaty in her eyes. *Don't spoil it! Don't destroy me!* she wanted to cry. Instead, she whispered dully: 'You'd better tell me, then, and get it over. Why shouldn't I marry Jason?'

'Because he's having an affair with a married woman.'

*   *   *

It seemed aeons instead of moments passed while Miranda stared with horror-filled eyes at her friend's unhappy face. At last she forced stiff lips to frame an almost soundless denial: 'I don't believe it. It's not true. It can't be.'

'I don't know,' Susan whispered hopelessly.

'Who?' Miranda clenched her hands. 'Who is she?'

'I don't know,' Susan repeated. She looked down at her own nervously twisting fingers. 'Rena wouldn't tell me. She said, "No names now – no trouble for me later if somebody talks out of turn." But she swears she's seen them together recently and she believes it's true.'

Miranda couldn't speak. Susan looked at her deathly white cheeks and trembled. She whispered: 'Are you all right? I'm sorry, but I *had* to tell you – I'd never forgive myself if afterwards it – it was true and you – you – because then it would be too late.'

Miranda bowed her head, then hid her face in her hands with a fierce, convulsive movement. 'It's too late now,' she choked. 'It's too late . . . I love him . . .'

CHAPTER SEVEN

A married woman . . .

There was little sleep for Miranda on that anguished eve of her wedding day. All through the long dark hours she tossed restlessly, Susan's disclosure, Jean's advice, and everything she had ever heard about Jason seething through her mind.

But it was all in the past, she told herself desperately, even if it was all true. The past, but not now. Logic tried to convince her that Rena's latest insinuation couldn't be true – hadn't she herself shared so many of his free evenings and week-ends since he asked her to marry him? With his work and all the rushed trip it entailed there could have been precious little time to spare for the alliance Rena claimed. Perhaps his name *had* been linked with that of a married woman – Rena Harvey would link anyone's name to intrigue at the merest whisper of hearsay – but that didn't mean it was still linked with ... *Who was she?*

Susan had gone, unhappily, and Jean had arrived back, to drag out the reason for the distraught state in which she found Miranda. She had been shocked and incredulous, then angry, and her advice blunt: 'Forget it, and trust him – or get on that phone and have it out with him.'

Miranda could do neither, and when Jason rang as promised at ten o'clock she could only respond in taut little syllables. The dreadful question stayed locked in anguish while she longed desperately for some assurance of his love, one that would banish these heartbreaking doubts. It seemed that something of what she felt got over to him, but that he drew the more obvious conclusion.

'I won't keep you – I feel a bit like that myself,' he said.

'Like what?' she quavered.

'Like you sound – somewhat *hors de combat*,' he returned dryly. 'But don't worry – tomorrow is all ours. Good night, sweetness. See you ...'

Sweetness ... She said the word softly to herself. It was the nearest he had ever come to an unguarded endearment that hinted at the depth of feeling she searched for in him; one that was not part of that brittle charm he sometimes adopted and which she had instinctively divined as partly protective as well as a man's artifice towards a woman. Because we are to blame for that artifice, she thought suddenly. We want a constant statement of affection, and a man will sometimes give it automatically. *Practised* ...?

She turned her head, searching out the dim outlines of the room with troubled eyes. This was the last time she would sleep here. Soon another girl would sleep and dream here in this bed. Would she ever lie awake until the small hours, tortured by indecision, wondering . . .? But what decision? The wedding was tomorrow. Everything was arranged. How could she back out now? With her heart crying out for him . . .

The dark curved hump that was Jean took shape in the bed at the far side of the window, stirred gently, then wriggled over.

'Miranda, are you *still* awake?

'Yes.'

'Well, go to sleep, for goodness' sake!' came the hissed command. 'Do you *want* to look a wreck on your wedding day?'

'I – I can't sleep. 'I don't know what to do.'

'I've told you – forget it. Suppose you did walk out on him and found it was just gossip after all? You should have told him what they're saying and given him the chance to deny it.'

The very thought sent cold tremors through Miranda. She knew instinctively what Jason's reaction would be: cold anger, and possibly curt dismissal of the whole matter. He would neither admit nor deny, of that she was sure, but it would mean the end of everything. With such an accusation between them what chance would there be for trust or love?

'Anyway, I've always thought there's a ghoulish motive behind that sort of gossip,' Jean went on. 'They love the satisfaction of destroying something they haven't got themselves.'

'But Susan isn't like that.'

'Maybe not, but she should have tried to pin down something a bit more concrete before she told you. Oh, surely you know how a rumour gets bits added to it as it passes along,' Jean said impatiently, heaving the coverlet back to her chin. 'Maybe he is friendly with a married woman. Maybe he's also friendly with her husband. Of course, if you're not much in love with him this would prove it. If you were really in love with him you'd want to tear out the eyes of anybody who said anything against him. I'd say it was jealousy, myself. And he did ring you all the way from Moscow . . . and all those flowers . . . that heavenly ring . . .' Jean's voice was getting sleepier. 'There's probably a very innocent explanation, and I know I wouldn't take anyone else's word for it. I'd want to find out for myself . . .'

There was stillness, and a soft sigh as Jean settled down again. Miranda stared up at the ceiling and tried to see things Jean's way. The numbness of exhaustion was taking over now and with it a certain clarity. Neither Jean nor Susan were entirely unbiased in their conviction, and neither could provide the answer. She could only seize at what her heart wanted to believe: that whatever relationships Jason had had in the past she was the present. She was the one he had chosen to become his wife . . . no one could take that away from her . . .

At last she fell into an uneasy sleep, which seemed to have lasted only moments when Jean touched her shoulder and said cheerfully:

'Wake up – morning tea for the bride!'

'What time is it?' Miranda struggle up, not yet back to reality, and gave a cry of dismay as she saw the bedside clock. *Half past eight!* And the taxi was coming at ten!

'Now dinna fret!' Jean pushed her back against the pillow. 'Everything's under control. You've five minutes to drink your tea while I run your bath. All you have to do is obey orders.'

Jean and Mrs. Saunders certainly had everything under control. Calmly and briskly, but without fuss, they organized that last hour and a half, keeping up a cheerful banter and never once giving Miranda a moment to consider that there had ever been the slightest doubt about her wedding taking place. Only once was the shadow of the night allowed to flit across the morning, and that was when Miranda, seated in front of the mirror, met her new friend's reflected gaze.

'You're going to need a touch of colour in those cheeks, I think.'

Mrs. Saunders overheard this and came to look. 'Wedding nerves,' she said. 'I looked exactly the same.'

'You, Auntie?' Jean giggled. 'I bet Uncle Andrew looked ten times worse.'

'Your Uncle Andrew had had such a night with the boys the night before it was a toss-up whether I married him or the best man,' Mrs. Saunders said tartly. 'Sometimes I wish I had,' she added darkly.

'Now you don't mean that,' said Jean.

'Maybe not now. But you never saw our best man. He—' Mrs. Saunders broke off with an exclamation and rushed out. She returned immediately with a handful of letters. 'Your post – I forgot to bring it up before. Here you are . . .'

There were several cards. From Jean and her aunt, from Susan and Ray, from several other girls in her office, from Rena Harvey, surprisingly wishing her every happiness, and one from Jason. It was a silver card, with no personal message except the strong black signature, and even though she knew this was yet another of the arrangements Miss Mayo had taken care of it brought a rush of warm emotion and a smarting to her eyes. Why hadn't she thought of this token herself? The final gesture before their lives were linked.

The thought of Jason's post arriving without a message from herself worried her for the rest of the short time that remained before the taxi swept Susan and herself off to Caxton Hall. Neither of them spoke during the journey, Susan was unusually quiet and wore a faint air of guilt, and Miranda felt chilled and trembling as she went into the building.

The first person she saw was Jason. He looked tall and distinguished in a dark formal suit and more devastatingly attractive than ever. As he came forward she scarcely noticed the older, heavily built man with the vaguely familiar face who was with him. For a moment Jason neither smiled nor spoke, and she could only look up into those disturbingly steady eyes, the hue of smoke-grey crystal, as long as they chose to hold her captive. She had no knowledge of the vision of pale, ethereal beauty she made, or the unconscious plea of her own wide eyes. Then Jason said: 'You look very lovely,' and broke the spell holding her in a trance.

She put out her hand. 'Do I? – I'm sorry I forgot to send you a card – thank you for yours.'

'Card?' His brows went up, then his companion moved forward and Jason turned. 'I don't think you've met Sir Charles Hubard, our chairman. Charles – this is my bride-to-be, Miss Meake.'

'And a very beautiful bride-to-be,' Sir Charles corrected, heavily jocular. 'I'm charmed to meet you, my dear – and I hope he deserves you. My wife should have been here by now, but—' he broke off, glancing past her. 'Ah here she is now.'

Sir Charles began introductions, and at the same moment the previous wedding party emerged and it was time for the brief ceremony which made Miranda into Mrs. Jason Steele.

She retained few memories of that wedding morning. She remembered Sir Charles clearing his throat as he bent to append his signature as witness, and again Sir Charles making the time-honour prompting: 'Well, kiss your bride, my boy!' and Susan's stifled giggle in the background while Jason's lips made what seemed like a perfunctory obedience and a camera flash exploded a blinding radiance over their heads.

Sir Charles' own chauffeur-driven limousine took them back to Byrne Square, and within its privacy Jason at last took her in his arms and without speaking claimed her lips with considerably more feeling.

Miranda wanted to cling to him, but her hands were still involved with the enormous beribboned silver horseshoe Susan had thrust at her as she got into the car. By the time she freed her fingers of the ribbons Jason had drawn back.

'Are you hating all this fuss too much?' he asked with brittle humour.

'No – of course not!'

She sounded so shocked he laughed. 'With all due respect to feminine dreams, I have to admit I'm thankful we decided against having all the trimmings. Frankly, imagination boggles at what might have been.'

'Does it?' she said in a small voice.

He took her left hand, twisting and working at the new gold band he had so recently placed on the third finger. 'Isn't this the main thing?' he said softly.

She looked down, the small sensuous movements compelling her heartbeat to quicken, even as she wondered if it were mockery rather than feeling behind the small question.

'All those ghastly time-worn traditions,' he went on musingly. 'Sly back-slapping; snide speeches about little troubles and coy gifts of miniature porcelain potties! Apart from endless confetti stuffed into every crevice they can find.' His mouth turned down at the corners. 'If Charles and Miss Mayo and Libby have failed to follow my intructions I'll fire the lot of them.'

'You can't fire Sir Charles!'

'Not literally, alas, but I'll find other ways of revenge.'

Miranda did not doubt this; even with all the bonhomie of a wedding day the ruthlessness she had alway known Jason possessed was merely dormant beneath the surface. Somewhat to her dismay, the inevitable little gift of porcelain had found its way among the wedding presents beginning to pile up at the house in Byrne Square. It was from Ray and Susan, tucked in with the stainless steel serving dish which she already knew they had planned to give her. There was a magnificent Georgian silver tray from Sir Charles and Lady Hubard, gay linen glass cloths from Jean and her aunt, a crystal bowl from Wally Ambrose, whom she knew by sight and who was waiting at the house with a group of men who were strangers.

'I passed the word round yesterday,' said the plump, genial Wally. 'Couldn't let you depart without a decent send-off.'

The 'decent send-off' included much of the back-slapping and snide jollification Jason had deplored, besides the generous imbibing of champagne and a great deal of kissing of the bride. It was plain that Wally and his colleagues had laid firm foundations of the party spirit before their arrival, and Jason made no secret of his thankfulness when the time came to leave for the airport.

Miranda came downstairs after changing into a cool blue linen suit more suitable for a flight and found Jason holding his guests at bay.

'No more! You can hijack my wine cellar but not my wedding flight. We'll make it without your help. Come on, Miranda, hurry!'

It was like running a gauntlet.

Sir Charles' limousine stood by the kerb, his impassive-faced chauffeur ready at the wheel, and in front of it stood Wally's vintage Daimler, decked with ribbons. The plan appeared to be to pressgang the bride and groom into this, and hands reached out to seize Miranda as she reached the top of the steps. Miss Mayo and Susan were struggling to get through, and Sir Charles was standing by his car, bellowing at his unruly executives. Suddenly Jason thrust himself in front of Miranda and snatched her up into his arms. A cheer went up as he fled down the steps and almost threw her into the back of the limousine as Sir Charles opened the door. Another moment, and Jason was safely inside and the door slammed shut. The car reversed quickly and pulled away to a chorus of cries, laughter, boos and a shout of 'Shame!' amid the well-wishes and the final hail of confetti. Sir Charles waved, and Susan ran along the pavement to wave the last frantic farewell.

It took a little time to recover their breath and most of the car journey to rid themselves of the endless confetti. Miranda was now strung to a high pitch of excitement and she had accepted the send-off as part of the day. Not so Jason, who made no secret of his sense of humour being decidedly strained.

'So much for a quiet wedding! Sorry about the roughing up.'

'But I didn't mind – it's all part of getting married.'

94

'Perhaps. But things get out of hand. If they'd had their way we would have missed the plane,' he said brusquely.

She could not deny this and deemed it wiser to remain in silent agreement. He was glancing at his watch, as though to reassure himself that there was no risk of that disturbing possibility, and the dark frown still hovered between his brows. Miranda watched it, and in that moment the beginning of wifely wisdom was born in her. She said firmly:

'We won't – now sit still a moment – there's confetti on your shoulder.'

Almost unwillingly he obeyed as she brushed at the dark lapels with feather-light fingers. She met his gaze, and his brows flickered.

'Will you forgive me if I say thank God it's over?'

'Of course,' she said seriously. 'I know exactly how you feel.'

'Do you, now? I wonder.' Suddenly amusement was back and the ruffled look had fled. He reached for her. 'I don't think you do, you know,' he added on a rather provocative note.

Deep within the tinted shadows of the smoothly speeding limousine she forgot all doubts as she let singing senses drown in response to his kiss. This moment was hers; this was her wedding day. Nothing, no one, could take that away from her . . .

* * *

The long transatlantic flight was smooth and without delays, and to Miranda a new and exciting experience. But not so to Jason, who was too seasoned a traveller for the experience to hold any novelty, nevertheless, he was indulgent of her eager pleasure and her shocked remonstrance when, after the brief stopover at Bermuda, he announced his intention of having a siesta.

'As I've seen it all before, and it seems even a husband can't compete with that' – a mocking wave of his hand – 'I'll leave you to it and catch up with some sleep.'

'I don't know how you can,' she breathed, gazing down at the blue and rose glory of the Caribbean spreading like a magic carpet far below the great plane.

'Can what?' he asked lazily, folding his arms and composing his head more comfortably against the padded curve. 'Sleep on my honeymoon?'

'No!' Instantly the warmth flowed into her cheeks at the sidelong glance accompanying his response. 'I mean, how can you ignore all that down there – even if you have seen it all before? It's so beautiful.'

'Wait till you see the sunset.' He closed his eyes and appeared to give every indication of fulfilling his intention of sleeping.

For a moment she was reminded of that other occasion when she had looked down on a sleeping Jason, and a tender smile curved her mouth. There was that same strangely vulnerable air about him, as though he shed the hard façade he donned for the world, and a rush of emotion engulfed her; how she loved him. The same little temptation returned, strong in her, to touch and smooth those fascinating silver wings in the dark hair at his temples, and her hand almost winged to temptation's bidding when the grey eyes opened and that disturbing gaze fastened on her face.

'Don't look at me like that – I can't,' he said, his expression not flickering.

She felt a tremor, even as her mouth framed the silent sweet query which she did not need answered.

'There are too many people on this plane, or I would.' His mouth quirked, and now his glance was outrageous. 'It'll be at least another four hours before we're alone.'

She folded her hands in her lap and broke the spell of his eyes, wishing the smiling stewardess hadn't chosen that precise moment on her return journey to pause and inquire if any refreshments were wanted.

'Not at the moment, thank you,' Jason dismissed, and then, in the same breath, 'you're blushing, my sweet.'

'What do you expect? she whispered indignantly. 'It's your fault.'

His white teeth glinted. 'I'm going to have to take a hell of a lot of blame, then. You blush a most endearing rose – must be the artist in me – it's a tint I want to keep on seeing.'

'I thought you wanted to go to sleep,' she reminded him, with the softest suggestion of reproach.

He gave a slight shake of his head. 'It's escaped me. I need someone to tell me a bedtime story.'

'Jemima Puddleduck? Or Brer Rabbit?'

'No, I grew out of them a long time ago.' He sought her hand and enclosed it in his strong warm clasp. 'I expected a more romantic suggestion from you, little Miss Meake.'

'Sleeping Beauty, or ...?' She lapsed in dreamy-eyed silence, for the moment too happy even to think.

'Who was awakened with a kiss ...? That's more in my line ...'

Even the mocking note, never absent for long from Jason's voice, could not destroy the enchantment. Those first few hours of tentative seeking into the man–woman relationship were the most delightful she had ever experienced. That weaving a spell of enchantment might be an art at which Jason was all too expert when he chose did not occur to her; she was too much in love to want to resist the magic, and too much in love to hide that fact successfully.

The glory of a crimson sunset over the Caribbean was as much as Jason had prophesied – even more. They dined high above the silver moonlit sea, and came down into the black velvet night and the myriad lights of Mexico City. There they encountered the first delay, and an hour-long wait for the flight which would complete their journey. Jason fumed, and Miranda once more remained in the silence of wisdom, and when at last they were airborne again he relaxed rather unwillingly and said wryly: 'If all travellers were as patient as you no one would ever get anywhere.'

After a few moments of reflection he said suddenly: 'There should be a small surprise waiting at the hotel for you.'

'A surprise?' she echoed. 'I didn't know one could arrange surprises from so far away.'

'You can arrange anything from anywhere if you know the way to go about it,' he said dryly.

He made no further mention of the matter, and she was left to speculate as to the nature of the 'surprise' which should be waiting at their destination. At last she gave up; it might be anything from a full-scale Mexican bridal reception to a boudoir of orchids! Jason was so unpredictable anything was possible; he was also, whatever faults he might have, extremely generous.

And then they landed. At last they were stepping down into the rich alien dark of the Mexican night, to new strange scents and sounds, to a sense of excitement that banished the traces of travel tiredness which had begun to steal unawares over Mirranda, despite her determination not to miss one single moment that life could offer.

Lights, music, neon and floodlighting bathing people and places in every hue imaginable. Flowers making the air heavy with their fragrance, laugher, gaiety, lovers both young and old, the necklace of reflected sparkles laid on the bosom of the ocean, and most potent of all, the almost tangible smell of wealth. Only the rich could afford to play long in Acapulco and any traces of poverty were soon swept from the streets.

Miranda was unaware that her hand had crept into Jason's and her eyes were unnaturally bright as the taxi stopped at the hotel and two small dark-eyed boys rushed to take out the cases. Wide glass doors swung open and a waft of cool air billowed out like an invisible curtain from a white and rose furnished reception hall, and instantly Jason was being accorded the attention he took as his right.

The kaleidoscope of impressions was still swirling colourfully in Miranda's brain when she found herself out of doors again, being escorted with Jason by the dark, voluble man who had greeted them. The path wound though gardens of plants that looked even more exotic under golden lanterns and starlight than she imagined they would appear under the sun and ended by a wide terrace of pink and blue crazy paving. There was an oval pool, dotted with floating blossoms, and beyond it the miniature villa into which the voluble little man ushered them.

It was all white inside, with vivid Mexican rugs scattered on the cool polished floors and boldly patterned curtains and cushions providing a brilliant contrast of traditional colours against the white. There was a lounge with wide garden doors giving on to the terrace and music playing softly from an as yet undiscovered source; a kitchenette fitted with a well stocked fridge and a miniature bar of drinks and ice-cold fruit juices; a big airy bedroom with its own half-moon terrace overlooking the sea, and a sugar-pink bathroom glittering with chrome and wide mirrors. There was a choice of three restaurants if they wanted to dine, or they could have their meals in privacy in the villa, the dark man told them; there was a bar in the centre of the main swimming pool where they could sit on a stool in the water and cool off as they sipped their drinks, and there was dancing on the Crystal Roof if they felt so inclined. And if there was anything they required . . . Oh, and the things the Señor had ordered had arrived; they were being brought over from the main hotel this minute.

Jason finally persuaded the little man that everything seemed to be perfect, while Miranda gazed around her in a state of bemusement. She hadn't taken it all in and the little man's steps had scarcely faded across the terrace before the retinue arrived bearing what seemed like dozens of enormous flat boxes, all white with tiny gold coronets stamped all over them and shiny gold ribbon tied across the lids. Jason gave calm directions, a discreet exchange of coins was made, smiles, flashed all round, and the little retinue departed. At last there was silence, except for the soft strains of music and the muted background sounds from the gardens and the hotel.

'Well, Mrs. Steele?' Jason sauntered in from the patio. 'Do you approve?'

'Of this? I'm overcome!'

'I thought you might prefer it to the more conventional hotel suite. One can relax more, I think. Well,' he folded his arms, 'supposing you fix your husband a drink. I'm exhausted.'

'Oh, yes!' Eagerly she hurried to the miniature bar, looking uncertainly at the unfamiliar brand names. 'What do you want?— Some of these look frightfully potent.'

'Iced lager.'

Her hands were trembling as she opened the can and poured it into a tall glass. Excitement and tension were beginning to take effect now and she felt light-headed and unsteady as she took the drink to him.

'None for you?' His brows lifted.

'No, I couldn't— Is that all right?'

'Fine – do you want anything more to eat tonight?'

'Do you?'

'Not particularly. But you didn't eat much on the plane.'

'I'm not hungry – I think I'd better start unpacking.'

He lolled back among the cushions. 'You'd better investigate those boxes.'

'Are – are all those – for me?' Her eyes were enormous.

'When you open them you'll see they're certainly not for me. Although,' his mouth curved wickedly, 'in a way they are.'

She hesitated, and then went slowly into the bedroom.

The boxes were stacked in a heap, beckoning and intriguing, in the middle of the white carpet, and the trembling of excitement possessed her again as she lifted the top one and looked at it for a long moment before she succumbed to curiosity and pulled the gold ribbon ties.

It was a little like opening Pandora's box, but with infinitely more attractive results. From under softest tissue floated a cloud of apricot gossamer which slowly settled into the folds of a negligée. She held it against herself, and then saw that the box was not yet empty. More layers of matching apricot tissue yielded undies of the same gossamer nylon, sheer, soft, sensuous, the kind of luxury wear Miranda's sensible, thrifty heart occasionally dreamed of but would have hesitated, even if she came into a fortune, ever to indulge in the extravagance of buying for herself.

In a kind of fever she delved into the boxes, one by one, little cries escaping her as each gave up their delight. Fairy cobweb lace in delicate lilac, slip, briefs, bra and nightdress ... a myriad tiny pleats of electric blue swirling from the white swansdown yoke of a negligée ... rose pink scattered with tiny rose-pearl stars ... lemon voile with long floating satin ribbon streamers ... a midnight blue creation of exotica, embroidered with silver orchids, that had its matching nightie and blue velvet bandeau, presumably for her hair ... each more exquisite than the other ...

'Are they the right size?' came Jason's voice lazily from the doorway.

'I – I think so. I haven't tried any on yet.' She was still bewildered, amid a sea of tissue paper and lingerie that was flowing over both beds and lapping the floor. 'But Jason ... You can't mean – not all these – there must be a fortune here. I can't possibly—'

'Do you like them?'

'Of course! They're exquisite. But—'

'I had to guess your size at a twelve,' he cut in, 'if they're not right they can be changed.'

She looked at him weakly and shook her head.

He touched the rose pink wrap with the tiny stars, and a faint smile curved his mouth. 'I thought of having you select your own choice back in London, then I decided those shy principles of yours might not allow you to accept rather intimate gifts before the circle of gold made it all in order.'

Her gaze dropped before the expression in his eyes, as she wondered if her reaction would have been quite as prim as he surmised. 'They're beautiful,' she whispered. 'You're too generous. I—'

'Is that the lot?' he cut in, suddenly abrupt, and turning over the heap of tissue and box lids. 'Have you opened them all?'

'I think so.' She bent over the tide of colour, startled by his change of tone. 'What's the matter? Have they sent the wrong—' Instantly she leapt to the conclusion that indeed a great mistake had been made. These weren't for her. These were intended for another visiting bride, or a film star, or a princess. The orders had got mixed . . .

'The idiots!' Jason swore, rapidly tossing the empty boxes into a corner. 'Somebody's slipped up. Half of it's missing.'

He turned and met her blank astonishment and gave a gesture of impatience. 'Look, darling. Surely it must be obvious. That damn girl . . . I wanted to play it your way. I guessed it mattered to you. And she's sent every colour under the sun except the important one.'

At last Miranda realized what he meant. Amid the exquisite hues only one was missing, the traditional bridal white. The fact that he had thought of this brought a sudden tightening in her throat and a smarting to her eyes. She turned away and began to make a brisk task of seeking hangers in the long fitted wardrobe to hang up the new trousseau. 'It doesn't matter,' she said chokily. 'I wouldn't change them for anything else, even as white as driven snow.'

There was no response, only the sounds of his own case being opened and unpacked.

She tried to laugh. 'I don't think I'll need to unpack – except my swimsuit.'

He only said, 'Are you going to unpack now? Or shower first?'

'I – I'd better unpack first,' she said slowly.

'Then I'll shower now.'

It seemed he had already unpacked, with the speed of one long practised in the traveller's art, for his case reposed on the rack and through the partly open bathroom door she could hear the chinking of toilet accessories being set on glass shelving. Suddenly she seemed to be in a muddle of possessions, and when the splashing sounds ceased she was still trying to organize her things. He strolled back in, his dark hair glistening and ruffled with moisture, clad in a dark blue towelling robe with white lapels and tie-sash. His brows went up as he surveyed her and the garments still strewn around, and he lounged down on the other bed.

'Want any help?'

'No, thanks, I can manage.'

He shrugged and continued to lounge there, watching her with half closed eyes. That silent, lazy regard began to wield a strange effect, making her feel awkward and unsure of herself, a self-conscious feeling becoming more pronounced with every passing moment.

'Leave it, for goodness' sake,' he said at last, and stretched out one hand. 'Come here.'

Suddenly she was painfully conscious of him, of his maleness, of all that this night should mean, and of a constraint that was almost fear of making her its prisoner.

'I'm almost finished – I can't leave all this untidiness.' She tried to retain a sense of normality, trying to put into words her own mental reassurance: 'If I come over there I'll never get anything organized tonight,' and laugh as she spoke.

But the small laughter refused to come convincingly, and at that moment she reached the last item in her case, the simple peignoir of pale blue seersucker and the little frilled nightdress she had bought along with the other items of her modest trousseau. They had seemed sweet and charming when she chose them with such care and respect for her slender budget, but now, in comparison with the luxury of Jason's gift, they seemed very ordinary, almost inferior.

'What's the matter?'

'Nothing.' She closed the case and put it on the rack beside Jason's, then hesitated before the wardrobe.

'Sure?'

'Sure.'

'But I don't think you are.' Soundlessly he had moved, to put his hands on her shoulders and turn her to face him. Her heart gave a choking little bump, and suddenly she desperately wanted reassurance. If only he would say that he loved her, if only he would make her forget this new frightening feeling that he was a stranger. *Make me love you!* she willed him silently. *Make my world right again* ... She raised a tremulous gaze to his face, pleading unveiled in her eyes.

'Has anyone told you how beautiful you looked today?' he said softly.

Her lashes dropped, to veil disappointment. 'You yourself – and Susan and Sir Charles.'

'Susan and Sir Charles!' Jason mocked softly. 'I do believe you're genuinely without vanity. What other virtues have I yet to discover in you, I wonder? Patience, modesty, meekness, innocence . . . I hope you're not going to bring out *too* much of the best in me.'

'You make virtues sound very dull.' The more obvious, trite riposte did not occur to her at that moment; had it done so she would not have voiced it. Again that wave of uncertainty carried her helplessly on it and the doubts were building their dark barrier round the man who had stormed her heart. Desperately she tried to banish them, to match the kind of mood he seemed to expect of her. 'But you've forgotten. I'm stubborn, and impertinent, and a whole lot of other things.' She forced a giggle. 'You said so yourself. Remember? The night I pitched camp in the sacred sanctum of the great white chief?'

Jason's brows narrowed, then crinkled with amusement. 'I did say some rather frightful things to you that night, didn't I? I'm still not sure how much they were deserved.'

His grasp tightened on her shoulders, pulling her against him, and the warm masculine smell of his lotions and shower talc entered her nostrils. She saw the brown skin of his throat and felt the vibrations of his voice as he added: 'Oh yes, you have unsuspected depths, my little nocturnal intruder, and I'm going to explore every single one of them . . .' His mouth came down hard on hers, stifling any reply she might have made, and now there was the sense of a long-pent restraint being cast aside.

The caressing hands slid across her back, warm and rough with impatience on the thin silkiness of her sleeveless top, communicating their urgency. He whispered something incoherent through the kiss, and then the frail barrier of thin jersey was no longer barring his seeking hands. His touch burned like fire on her skin and when the soft sigh of triumph escaped him she stiffened.

'Scared of me already, Miranda?' he whispered huskily.

'No – but I'm not ready – I haven't showered,' she said wildly, slipping out of his grasp.

He closed his eyes despairingly as she tugged at the dishevelled top. 'Go on,' he sighed, and turned away.

She snatched up her wrap and toilet bag and fled into the shower room. Like one in a fever she brushed her teeth, showered and talced herself before she was properly dry, and fought out a crazy mental dialogue with herself all the time. Crazy to sigh with relief as she pulled the nightdress on and thrust herself in the wrap. Why should she fear his coming in while she was naked? She knew what marriage meant. She was in love with him – she shouldn't be shy or afraid of him ...

She tied back her hair, and her fingers and toes felt icy, despite the heated atmosphere. In the mirror her eyes were wide and darkly brilliant, and the girl reflected there looked like a stranger. Abruptly she turned away and forced herself to calm. She dabbed skin fragrance on wrists and temples and walked back into the bedroom.

Jason had retired. He lay back, his hands behind his head, a single sheet pulled up to his bare chest.

He eyed her without moving, his expression enigmatic.

She paused uncertainly. 'My hair got soaked in the shower.'

His brows moved non-committally. 'Feel better?'

'Mm.' She fiddled with the sash of her wrap, then suddenly realized her blunder. Without thinking she had grabbed the prim little blue seersucker night things; the exquisite creations that were Jason's gift still hung in the shadows of the wardrobe. The stab of dismay made her bite her lip and give a distraught exclamation. She turned towards the white panelled doors, then back to the silent man.

'Oh, Jason, I was going to try them all on, and then—' again she caught at her lower lip in distress.

'It's a bit late for a modelling session,' he said coolly. He reached for the switch of the light above his bed. 'You'd better turn in.'

Every aspect of his attitude seemed to denote that he was only waiting for her to climb into the other twin bed before he switched off his own light and settled down for the night. In the grip of a new bewilderment, she stared at his dark lean features. 'But – but—' she stammered through parted lips.

'But what?' he said, almost cruelly.

She shook her head, unable to credit the change in him a few minutes had wrought.

'It – it's our wedding night,' she whispered at last.

'I hadn't forgotten.'

For long moments she faced his cool gaze, then she bent her head. Nothing had prepared her for an eventuality such as this and she was totally at a loss how to deal with it. She turned away, undoing the sash of her wrap and slipping out of the garment. She dropped it over a chair and stood stiffly, a slender, uncertain little figure in the demure frilled nightdress.

'Miranda.'

Slowly she turned, her face pale and set, and saw him watching her with all the old cynicism in his eyes. He said flatly, 'I've little taste for duty sex, Miranda, nor does the old vestal virgin sacrifice hold much appeal at the moment. Oh, yes,' his mouth curved ironically as the shocked protest sprang to her lips, 'I knew from the moment I met you how it would be with you, but I—'

'*Then why did you marry me?*'

'You didn't hear me out,' he retorted dryly, seemingly unprovoked by the impassioned retort. 'I was going to say I was perfectly confident that it wouldn't always be like that – even though it all goes back full circle to this loving and trusting business. Even though you've married me you don't trust me, do you?'

'I do!' she denied hotly. 'I—'

'You're not a very convincing fibber – but I'm not going to argue.' He sighed and his head sank back. 'For the moment let's just say that the past forty-eight hours have been a hell of a long haul – I haven't got the vodka out of my bloodstream yet – and leave it at that.'

'I understand,' she said quietly, trying to find reassurance from this statement and failing dismally. 'You must be travel-weary.'

'I am not travel-weary. Nor am I particularly tired,' he said grittily. 'But I'm not in the mood for a long, leisurely wooing. So I'd advise you to get your beauty sleep – in case I change my mind.'

She felt a strange slackness in the pit of her stomach. 'If that's the way you want it . . .'

'It is, and if you're honest you'll admit it's the way you want it, too.'

Denial choked in her throat, and in silence she crept into the other bed, to curl up into a small forlorn bundle. She heard the click of his bedside lamp, and dark silence descended on the room.

She stared wide-eyed into the night, straining to pick out the soft, even sounds of Jason's breathing, and all inclination for sleep deserted her. Like watching a playback in slow motion, she relived the hours since the wedding ceremony and tried to pin down the exact moment when the magic of enchantment had flown.

But the answer eluded her and instead came the old invasion of memories; from those first moments of knowing Jason Steele. Those cynical, heart-chilling tones saying: '*I like women . . . but when I want amusement . . . not with scared little innocents straight out of a Victorian sermon . . .*'

Did he still see her like that? Was that why he spoke mockingly of unsuspected depths? Did he already regret their marriage? A deep shuddering sigh convulsed her body. The past twenty-four hours had proved an effective antidote to the poison of Susan's disclosure, but now the fear returned in full force. Was Jason involved with a married woman? Was this where his heart truly lay?

Miranda turned over fiercely and buried her face in the pillow. She mustn't think this way. Once, perhaps, she might have believed Jason capable of such a liaison, even though her principles would hate accepting the knowledge, but not now. For if he loved one woman, who wasn't free, what possible motive could he have for marrying another, thus putting himself even further out of reach of his love?

But despite her despairing attempts to keep fear at bay one question throbbed in her brain. Had she made a dreadful mistake? For though she loved Jason with all her heart, she felt totally inadequate when she compared herself with the other women who had glittered in his life. However was she to hold the interest of a man like Jason? A self-confessed explorer of feminine society.

She hadn't made a very good start.

CHAPTER EIGHT

It seemed that sleep would elude her for ever during those long, miserable hours, even though a deadly lassitude gradually crept through her body, leaving only her mind and her emotions achingly awake.

Once she heard Jason stir. She held her breath, wondering if he were wakeful, and wished with all her heart that he would murmur across the darkness, something from which she could take comfort. But he didn't, and she fell again into forlornness. Surely this was the most cruel kind of loneliness. Alone, yet not alone. She sank down again and pulled the light coverlet up over her face.

The next thing she knew was a sudden awakening and that moment of startled awareness that comes with the comprehension of surfacing to an alien surrounding. She sat up and saw that the screens were still shaded, although all the sounds outside denoted that a holiday play-day was in full swing again. Then she realized she was alone. She grabbed her watch, gasped with disbelief and held it to her ear. It must have stopped. It couldn't be *three o'clock*!

But it hadn't stopped, and it was definitely day outside. She scrambled out of bed, found the bathroom empty, Jason's blue robe on a hook behind the door, and the emptiness of the *casita* not her imagination. Panic speeded her footsteps into the other rooms and slowed them as she returned to the bedroom. Where was Jason?

Hastily she showered, dressed and did her hair, and though she was aware of acute thirstiness she did not stop to find something to drink before she hurried outside.

The heat hit her like a hot dry blanket as she came into the brilliant sun. The sky was cloudless, the gardens blazed brilliant colours and lush green, and the pool reflected the dazzling cerulean heavens, dappled with floating pink blossoms and shimmers of sun-gold. Now that it was daylight she could see her immediate surroundings and for a moment interest overcame more painful emotions.

The main bulk of the hotel lay to her left, some distance away. The terraced gardens stretched from it in a long broad half-moon shape that curved above a steep rocky hillside overlooking the bay, and dotted along the half moon were several more *casitas* similar to the one accommodating herself and Jason. They were all white, with gaily painted shutters and sun awnings shading the little crazy paving patios, and each one had its own small pool. As she turned her head she saw a boy and girl emerge from the next *casita*, some twenty yards distant, and stroll to their pool. They paused on the edge of the pool, sat down on the ledge and suddenly turned into each other's arms, their mouths blending in a deep, sensuous kiss. Still bound together, they slid into the sparkling water and came up laughing, oblivious of any eyes which might observe, to drift in the pool and continue their lovemaking.

Abruptly Miranda swallowed hard and turned away. The lost

feeling closed round her again and she could not bear to watch the uninhibited joy of one another in the young lovers. Quickly she unbuttoned the brief pale green beach dress she had donned on top of her own bikini and dipped one toe into the pool. If Jason had taken off somewhere on his own she might as well take advantage of the once-in-a-lifetime occasion of having one's own personal swimming pool.

It was deliciously cool, and she swam round leisurely, trying to tell herself that she didn't care, and she'd die before she ever let Jason see that she cared. But somehow she wasn't very successful, and when she saw the shadow fall across the water and saw him looking down at her a rush of tears came to her eyes.

'Breakfast is on its way over,' he said. 'You'd better come out.'

No hand to help her out, only the long cool appraising stare as she clambered up and stood streaming, remembering she'd forgotten to bring a towel outside and praying that the tears would be lost in the droplets glistening on her cheeks. Then his remark sank in. Breakfast!

'You mean tea, don't you?' she said chokily. 'You might have let me know you were going off for the day.'

'Tea? The day?' His dark brows lowered. 'What *are* you talking about?'

'Don't try to be funny.' She walked past him, into the cool dimness of the *casita* and snatched up a towel. Avoiding him, she wrapped the towel round herself and stalked outside again.

'You have got out on the wrong side this morning.' He laid hands on her shoulders, as though to begin drying movements. 'Want any help?'

'No, thank you,' she said tartly. 'I can—' She stopped as she saw the little Mexican maid coming along the path and pushing a neat covered trolley. Deftly she began to unload china, dishes of prepared fruit, little rolls in a basket, and a large jug of coffee, setting them on a small table on the patio and drawing up two chairs in readiness.

'*Señora* . . .' The black eyes sparkled inquiringly as the little maid reeled off a bewildering list of items and awaited Miranda's decision.

'She's asking if you want French, English, American or Mexican breakfast,' Jason said helpfully when the silence had lengthened somewhat.

Miranda's lips tightened with exasperation. 'Listen, I know I slept in, but you don't need to carry things this far. Tell her I just want fruit and rolls with my coffee.'

Jason shrugged and spoke to the girl, who smiled and set out the things. Jason sat down, reaching for the coffee-pot, and asked: 'What time did you think you woke up?'

'Three o'clock.' She would not look at him.

'Three o'clock!' He laughed shortly. 'You know what you forgot, don't you?'

When she failed to reply he glanced at her. 'You forgot to adjust your watch to Central Time – there's six hours' difference. Three o'clock!' he taunted.

'I knew about that,' she returned stiffly. 'But I decided to leave it till I got here and alter my watch when I wound it last night. Instead of moving it on every hour or so.'

'Then you forgot.'

Suddenly she wished he would take that superior grin off his face. Was that all he could talk about? Her foolishness over such a small matter? With trembling fingers she split and buttered a roll, and exclaimed sharply: 'So what? What does it matter?'

The effect she had wished for was achieved. The grin vanished and chill came into eyes. 'True.' He shrugged. 'What does it matter?'

In silence he helped himself to black coffee and unfolded his newspaper. The chill crept perceptibly across the table, and Miranda forgot her brief spasm of pique. The mouthful of roll threatened to choke her and all the memories of the previous night rose up again to taunt and disparage. She began to feel like a child who knows it has failed, in spite of its longing to please, and again she began the despairing self-interrogation. Why had she experienced that instinct to evade Jason last night, allowed it to prevent her responding when he started to make love to her? It would be stupid to deny those brief, bewildering moments of evasion, or deceive herself into believing that he had not sensed them, and even more stupid to deny the effect he had on her . . . Just the thought of his touch sent tremors coursing through her and brought instant awareness of those hitherto latent desires he had wakened to compelling power.

She was no nearer an answer, or the way to breaking the barrier she sensed between them this morning, when he folded the paper and announced coolly:

'I've ordered a car. I thought you might like to explore the town.' He stood up and strolled to the side of the pool. 'It'll be here in about fifteen minutes, so you'd better change.'

Without response she did as he bade. When she emerged he was still standing there, having apparently not moved from his idle stance.

'Ready?' He picked up his sunglasses from the patio table and donned them as he moved forward.

The big dark lenses added further to his enigmatical disposition and she sighed as she walked with him to where the car waited on the sweep in front of the hotel.

There were many sights to engage her interest that day. The luxurious shops and trendy cafés to attract the tourists, the occasional glimpses of the little thoroughfares behind the wealthy façade where the true town had its daily existence in shabby apartment houses that seemed to lean towards each other under the weight of balconies festooned with flower boxes and lines of washing.

Jason had booked a table for lunch at a restaurant overlooking the sea, and from where she was sitting Miranda could see right across the bay to the lush green of the hills that rose steeply all round the almost land-locked natural harbour. It was a breathtaking view, and only one of many she was to encounter as they continued their exploration. But the intangible barrier remained, marring what would otherwise have been a day of intense joy of discovery.

As the afternoon ended she began to feel hot, sticky and tired, and she was not sorry when Jason said it was time to make their way back to the hotel. He announced his intention of showering and having a swim in the huge main pool at the far side of the hotel, but as they got out of the car Jason heard his name called by a surprised voice and swung round to find a burly, middle-aged man advancing towards him.

The newcomer proved to be an American business acquaintance of Jason's, and when he discovered the nature of the occasion he insisted that Miranda and Jason should be his guests for dinner that evening.

'It's got to be tonight,' he said, smiling at Miranda with that easy friendliness most Americans seemed able to adopt towards someone newly met. 'I'm checking out in the morning. Now, Jason, don't look so reluctant! I insist! This is one occasion we've got to celebrate.'

His name was Don, and Miranda took to him immediately, despite the faint reluctance she thought she sensed in Jason. Over drinks he talked of his own family back in Oakland, of his own daughter's approaching wedding and the hectic preparations for it, and quizzed Miranda gently about her background. When they parted, after arranging to meet later in the evening, Miranda was feeling less despondent than earlier in the day.

'What are *clavadistas*?' she asked Jason as they changed for dinner. 'Don said something about seeing them tonight.'

'They're divers.' Jason said no more, intent on his reflection as he settled the lapels of his immaculate dinner jacket.

He looked more darkly saturnine than ever in slim-fitting dark pants and the contrasting white jacket, and suddenly she wished she could go into his arms, to be held hard against his heart and feel the warm smooth skin of his lean jaw-line under her fingertips. But she could not make the first move, the fear of a repulse was too great, and with a small sigh she added the finishing touch of perfume, then surveyed her reflection critically.

She was wearing a long flowing skirt of wine red panne velvet and a close-fitting blouse of white lace with tiny lace-covered buttons down the front and a wide deep vee neckline that moulded her firm young breasts and revealed the pearly smoothness of her shoulders. Her hair was drawn back sleekly and secured with a wine velvet ribbon bow at the nape of her neck, and she was suddenly confident that she looked her best. Her heartbeats quickened as Jason ran an appraising glance over her, but he made no comment, beyond a 'Ready?' accompanied by the now familiar lift of dark brows, and the tremulous heartbeats slowed again with disappointment.

Her host, however, had no such restraint. Don Westford paid her the homage of admiration in the nicest possible way, but brought the warm rush of rose into her cheeks when he remarked on Jason's fortune in winning himself so charming a young bride.

It was a wonderful meal, with a genial man who was a born host, in a wonderfully romantic setting. Their table was placed on a lamplit terrace right on the edge of a towering cliff which overlooked a deep inlet far below. The sea rushed and roared against the base of the cliffs, as though it would rend the rocks apart, booming its power and sending great curls of spume high into the air. Lights beneath caught those tossing plumes in their rays and lent them a ghostly radiance, and for a few moments Miranda leaned over the rail and watched, fascinated.

She was feeling a little more relaxed now and a little bit happier. The soft glow of the lamp amid the flowers on the table touched her cheeks with a beautiful luminous rose and revealed the soft appeal in her eyes of which she was quite unaware. The champagne began to lend its own particular magic, and when it was time for the *clavadista* to appear she gave an incredulous gasp.

'He isn't going to dive from *there*!'

Don nodded, and silence came along the terrace as the slender youth clambered lithely up to a pinnacle of rock high on the cliff opposite the terrace. In his hands he held two flaring torches, and poised there, motionless. Then the torches arced above his head as he sprang and flowed into a spectacular wake of brilliance that plummeted like a falling star to the water, more than a hundred feet below.

Miranda blinked, and many other throats echoed the sigh she gave.

'The water's only about three fathoms deep there, I believe,' Don said. 'Fantastic.'

'Is – is he all right?' she whispered, looking fearfully down towards the cove.

'Till the next performance.' Jason leaned over, his profile carved by the lamplit shadows. 'Yes, there he is.'

The *clavadista* was scrambling ashore now, clambering over the rocks and disappearing out of Miranda's range of vision.

It was almost time to go; the cigars were burning down and that sense of satiety after a rich meal and good wine had stolen imperceptibly over the party. The two men conversed in a lazy, desultory way as they returned to the hotel, and Miranda said good-bye to Don with a sense of genuine regret for a new friendship so soon parted. Would he see them in London soon? Would they ever take up his invitation to visit him and his family next time business took Jason to the States. If all the short friendships we made became permanent what countless friends we would have, she thought as Jason opened the *casita* door and stood aside for her to enter.

'You're very quiet,' he said, switching on the floor lamp in the lounge. 'You didn't begrudge an evening spent with old

Don, did you?'

'Oh no!'

She spun round so quickly with the denial she bumped against him. As quickly, his hands closed over her shoulders. She shook her head vehemently. 'I enjoyed the evening immensely. Didn't you?'

'Shall we say it was an ideal detour?'

Without waiting for her reply he bent his head and kissed the mouth that had parted in puzzlement at his somewhat odd remark. 'You looked very beautiful tonight,' he murmured a few moments later, and once again gave her no opportunity of response.

Instinctively she had stood still within his arms, then a tremulous joy came like a pain, so great it was, and her heart began to race. Slowly she let her hands steal up to his shoulders, still shy in their response, and instantly his embrace tightened. A wild sweet enchantment rippled through her veins as his mouth moved over her cheek, down to her throat, and left its trail of fire across her shoulder, and through it she sensed the languorous restraint keeping a rein on passion. The knowledge that he was trying not to rush her into a headlong surrender brought its own welling of love, so that when his questing hands found and began to deal with eight demure little lace buttons she stayed passive in the circle of his arm, her brow against his cheek, and felt him sigh softly.

'Still shy of me?'

She pressed her face into his shoulder. 'Not exactly. But . . . it's the first time in my life a man's undressed me.'

'I'm well aware of that.' His voice was husky. 'Does it seem so outrageous?'

'Not if – not if you're not madly impatient with me, and – and—'

'And what?' He found the ribbon bow, pulled it free, loosened the silky hair into abandon through his fingers. 'Go on, my prim little bride. Talk it all out while you get used to the idea of all these first times between a man and a woman.'

Her hand stilled in the thick vibrant hair she had always longed to run her fingers through. 'But it's only me, isn't it, Jason? It isn't the first time for you.' She thought she detected a tension in him and went on hurriedly: 'I don't mean that – try to understand – I accept that you must have known other women, had affairs with them before you met me, but I haven't.

That's why I – I'm not sure what you expect of me.'

'I think those are seas we shouldn't venture upon,' he said softly. 'I won't deny my past, but it's the last thing I want to remember at this moment.'

She knew a wild relief; Jason's past was the last thing she wanted to intrude on her thoughts this night. Almost feverishly she pressed her face against his. 'It's just that I – I don't want to fail you,' she whispered.

'Who said anything about failure?' He buried his mouth in her hair. 'I didn't.'

'Yes, but last night . . . why did you say . . .?'

'What did I say?'

'That you – that I didn't—' Her mouth parted despairingly under the onslaught of another. Jason was losing patience at last and he was making it very difficult for her to think straight, let alone talk straight.

'You didn't what?'

'I didn't appeal to you?'

'That was last night – and totally out of context. Do you always quote people out of context, my love?'

'No, but . . .' Through the intoxication of pagan senses beginning to clamour their delirious response she still strove to clear the doubts he had sowed the previous night. 'I – I didn't mean you thought I didn't want you. I—'

'I don't think you're very sure of anything at this moment,' he said softly.

But his words held an absent tone, that of a man distracted by more important matters than argument, and she looked up tremulously. 'I just wanted you to know . . .'

'I'm getting the message . . .' His lips moved against her ear and his hands played the music of love. 'Haven't you heard . . .? *To everything there is a season* . . .? Last night wasn't our moment.' He cupped one hand under her chin and upturned her face, staring down at her with shadowy eyes. The night stilled, then abruptly he gathered her bodily into his arms and almost fiercely buried his face in the sweet pearly softness of her breast. 'But this is . . .'

*   *   *

In the warm scented darkness of the Mexican night her doubts and fears had dissolved. Her body drowsed, luxuriating in this new and wondrous sense of well-being, while her mind revelled in the dual joys of surrender and possession. She wanted to talk, while her hand cradled Jason's dark head where it rested on her breast.

'Mm . . .?' he said sleepily.

'We'd better send our cards tomorrow – or we'll be home before they are.'

'Mm, does it matter?'

'Not really.' She gazed up into the darkness. 'We mustn't forget to send Libby one.'

There was no response, beyond a slight stirring and deeper settling of the dark head.

'Jason . . .?'

'Mm?'

'Do you think Libby will mind?'

'Mind what?' There was the suggestion of a sigh.

'Me. I mean, she's had the running of your home for a long time.'

'Why should she?' Jason's shoulders rose slightly, then slumped in contented relaxation. 'Not going to sleep, woman?'

'I can't.' Her mouth sent a secret smile up into the night. 'Time's too precious to waste in sleep. Don't you realize? – one whole day and nearly two nights have gone already. We've only four days. I don't want them to go too quickly.' She gave a deep sigh. 'I don't want them to go at all.'

He moved, so abruptly she was startled, and propped himself upon on one elbow. He looked down at the pale luminous oval of her face framed in the dark hair tumbled wantonly across the pillow and lifted one tress. 'Your eyes have lights in the dark – why are you laughing?' he demanded, his caress stilling in her hair.

'I'm not really.' She shook her head and raised one hand to touch his cheek. 'I've just found out that one thing I heard seems to be true.'

'Oh?'

'Men usually want to go to sleep afterwards.'

'And women always want to chatter.' His voice took on a husky note. 'Have I made you happy?'

'Very.' With all the honesty of her young heart she reached up impulsively and drew him down to her, to whisper against his cheek: 'If only I'm able to make you as happy!'

His mouth moved in search of her own. 'Is that so impossible a task?'

It was a question which, a few hours previously, she would have pondered on long and despairingly before venturing to seek its answer, but now, the warm urgency of his arms claiming her again, she let her silent lips give the other sweet answer he demanded.

His question must wait: only time could bring its answer.

CHAPTER NINE

'I'LL be late tonight,' said Jason, picking up his briefcase. 'Don't wait up.'

'As late as that?' Despite her resolution never to become a nagging wife or an inquisitor, Miranda could not keep disappointment out of her eyes. She pressed her fingertips against the place on her cheek which a troublesome neuralgia had made tender for the past two days and forced a smile. 'I'll leave the little light on for you if you're not back by the time I fall asleep.'

'The man from I.A. Components is due in late this afternoon. We'll be dining him at my club. But he's going on to Brussels tomorrow, then things may quieten down for a few days, my sweet. We'll have a night out.' He turned to stoop and drop a light kiss on the forlorn little mouth, and said abruptly: 'Is that tooth still bothering you?'

'A little bit,' she evaded his searching glance. 'I had it filled just the week before I left Evesham – that's still only about four months ago. I can't understand it; it looks all right.'

'You'd better make an appointment to have it seen to straight away,' he said firmly. 'Do that this morning.'

'Yes, Jason,' she nodded.

She stood by the window and watched the Mercedes nose out of the square. The forlorn droop stayed stubbornly across her shoulders, and she could not pretend that it was entirely due to the toothache which had disturbed her sleep for two nights.

Another late night!

She had been married exactly four weeks and five days, thirty-three days to be exact, and Jason had spent fifteen of them away from home. Admittedly they'd been in short breaks of two or three-day duration, but that didn't make it any more bearable when she considered that out of the remaining eighteen he'd been kept late by business conferences for three of them, a board meeting for one of them, and yet another taken by a flying trip to the Midlands for the annual general meeting of the governing board of the children's home – which he couldn't skip. It had been three in the morning when he'd got back from that session. Now she was beginning to realize what he had meant when he objected to spending their honeymoon within too convenient reach of the office!

In the way things happen, they'd ganged up, waiting for his return. There had been a packed appointment book, a round of E.E.C. meetings, a crisis caused by a shock merger looming suddenly on the business world's horizon, and Wally had had a minor accident which had made necessary a brief stay in hospital. And then there had been the business with Inger Minerals, Inc.

Miranda sighed. She'd thought the hectic phase was over. Apparently it wasn't. Slowly she went through the hall, let in the little grey tabby cat who seemed to have adopted her, and then went in search of aspirins. She should do as Jason bade her and not put off visiting the dentist, but she hadn't got round to finding a new one – it wasn't six months since her last check-up, she told herself, hating to admit that like a great many other people the thought of the dentist gave her the shivers.

'I couldn't face it this morning,' she murmured aloud to the little cat as she poured herself the last of the breakfast coffee and downed two aspirins.

No, not this morning, the little cat seemed to purr as she leaped soundlessly up into Miranda's lap for a few minutes of feline luxury before Libby arrived to clear the breakfast things.

Had anyone ever warned Miranda that marriage could bring its own kind of loneliness she would have received the warning with scepticism. For wasn't the whole essence of marriage in its loving and sharing and companionship? Not that she believed that marriage conferred constant companionship, but wasn't there always the knowledge that the other was there, the chosen one who made up that wonderful extension of one's own life?

She finished the coffee and stroked the little cat's soft fur, unaware that she sighed again. No matter how she tried to cling to that ideal belief it still wasn't quite enough consolation for the long hours when Jason wasn't there.

The kitchen door opened and shut with the now familiar

click and crump which meant Libby had come up again from her own flat which Jason had had converted from the lower ground floor. Originally the servants' quarters in Edwardian days, nothing of that dark comfortless atmosphere remained in the spacious three-roomed flat with every modern fitting in which Jason's housekeeper lived. Miranda hastily pushed the cat off her knees and began to stack the dishes on the trolley.

'You should have left those for me, Mrs. Steele,' Libby rebuked, hurrying across the kitchen and pulling a tea towel off the rail as she passed.

'I haven't anything special to do this morning.' Miranda splashed wash-up liquid liberally into the bowl. 'Anyway, I have to learn to housekeep some time. I couldn't bear to become a useless wife.'

Libby smiled faintly but made no comment. After a moment she asked if there were any particular requirements for the day's menu.

'No, it's another non-occasion tonight,' Miranda said resignedly, 'so I'll just make myself a sandwich.'

'It's no more trouble to make a meal for one than two,' Libby said equably. 'What would you like?'

'Jason to eat it with me,' was the wry rejoinder.

Libby tilted her head sympathetically. 'You married an important man, you know. He's never had a great deal of free time the years I've worked here.'

'Sometimes I wish he weren't quite so important,' Miranda sighed. 'I know he carries a tremendous responsibility, but he drives himself too—' She stopped. 'Was that the door bell?'

Libby was already moving. 'I'll get it.'

The moments passed. Miranda rested her hands on the edge of the sink. She could hear the exchange of voices, but the distance of the kitchen from the front of the house effectively blurred what was being said. Presently Libby's light brisk steps came along the rear hall.

'It's Mrs. Lindsterne, madam.'

Something in the housekeeper's tone made Miranda frown and look at her sharply. 'Mrs. . . .? Should I know her?'

'I couldn't say, madam.' Formality had returned like an easily assumed mask to the housekeeper. 'I could say that you're about to go out, if you're too busy to talk to her.'

'No . . .' Miranda reached for a towel to dry her hands. 'I'd better go and see what she wants. She's probably someone . . .'

she left 'Jason knows' unspoken and gave Libby another puzzled glance. Libby had sounded almost evasive – or was she imagining things? She obviously knew the caller, but if Mrs. Lindsterne was someone Jason knew why hadn't she said so?

Miranda hurried along the hallway. For some stupid reason her heart was beating quickly enough for her to be aware of it, and the odd little prickles of unease were making her feel stiff and tense. She paused by the mirror for a quick look at herself and drew a deep breath before she opened the lounge door to meet the newcomer.

The girl rose gracefully from the brocade chair near the window and came forward quickly towards Miranda. In those brief moments Miranda took in a tall slender form, blue-clad in simple, expensive elegance, sleek ash-blonde hair coiled about a well-poised head, a direct blue gaze and a self-confident smile, and the rainbow chips of dazzle from the diamond ring on the hand held out to Miranda.

'Do forgive me for bursting in on you at this ungodly hour, and without a word of warning, but I found myself a little early for an appointment and decided I must call,' the newcomer said with disarming friendliness. She bit gently at a full red lower lip. 'I haven't goofed, have I? You *are* Jason's wife?'

'Yes – Mrs. Lindsterne.' Feeeling oddly at a loss for words Miranda took the proffered hand and added, 'Please sit down.'

'Thank you – my name's Alicia, but my friends call me Lissa.' Another disarming smile as she gracefully sat down. 'I won't outstay my welcome, I promise, but I've been longing to meet you. You see we were away, cruising the Greek Isles, at the time of your marriage, and we were terrifically surprised when we got back a couple of weeks ago and heard Jason was married. We're old friends – he and my husband are Wykehamists – I don't know if Jason has spoken of us, but I simply had to call and offer our congratulations.' She hesitated, and pretended breathlessness. 'You see now what James means when he says I talk too much.'

'Not at all,' said Miranda politely. The newcomer had an engaging way with her, one that made the barriers of strangeness frail things in a very short time, despite the accent which Miranda described to herself as distinctly plummy. She smiled and admitted frankly: 'I can't recall Jason speaking of you or your husband, but possibly he did and with the rush and everything I forgot. Have you time for some coffee, Mrs. Lindsterne?' she invited.

'I'd adore some coffee – but please call me Lissa. Everyone does.'

Miranda went to tell Libby to bring the coffee and Lissa made herself at home with unfeigned pleasure. She launched into an account of the Greek Island holiday, a racy account that seemed to take for granted that Miranda was as familiar with the terrain as herself. Only when Libby came in with the tray did Lissa falter, and a glance passed between her and the housekeeper.

By chance Miranda intercepted that glance and experienced again that odd tremor of puzzlement. Surely she was imagining challenge in Lissa's eyes, and cool disapproval in Libby's. Then in a flash it had gone, and Lissa remarked in her self-possessed voice: 'Libby never forgets. Isn't she a darling? She remembers that I like my coffee black with a dash of cream.'

Libby laughed as she turned away. 'I keep a list in the kitchen of the likes and dislikes of all Mr. Steele's guests. It's the only way to remember.'

There was a silence after she closed the door behind her, and it had almost reached the stage of being awkward when Lissa set down her cup. 'Are you and Jason free the week-end after next?' she asked abruptly.

'I – I'm not sure.' Miranda was slightly taken aback. 'I am, but I don't know about Jason.'

'He'll have to be. I want you to come to us that week-end. We'll have a party to celebrate your wedding.' Lissa's voice quickened with enthusiasm. 'Everyone's longing to meet you – they're all saying how typical of Jason to leave everybody out of it and just secrete you away like that. He is naughty!'

Inwardly Miranda winced with mirth. If only Jason could hear himself described as 'naughty'! But she warmed to Lissa's enthusiasm despite this and murmured, 'It's very kind of you. May I let you know?'

'I'll leave you my number.' Lissa delved into her expensive black suede handbag. 'Now promise. You will come. Tell Jason he has to keep that week-end free. Heavens! I must dash. I'm late.'

The lounge seemed quite empty and quiet when she had gone. Only a faint drift of *Hermès* lingered for a brief while, and the tinge of coral on the rim of the white china coffee cup.

Miranda stood there in the centre of the room, her eyes thoughtful as she looked at the card her unexpected visitor had left, then she put it on the mantelpiece and took the tray of coffee things along to the kitchen. Libby had gone out to shop, and Miranda suddenly decided to go out and do some shopping herself. She left a note telling Libby not to bother preparing any lunch, and spent a leisurely morning window-shopping before having a light snack lunch at the Corner House.

It was still a novelty to her to be free during the daytime shopping hours and not have to rush round getting everything in on Saturday, when all the shops didn't stay open. It was bliss to have time to dawdle, to look at things and make comparisons, and not have to keep a mental eye constantly on the clock. She had a sudden impulse to buy some small gift for Jason, after-shave or talc, or one of those fat cakes of soap on a rope for the tub. She wandered round Selfridges, chose some splash cologne and herbal bath oil, and then browsed happily in the record department where she indulged herself in a long-coveted album of Chopin piano music.

The afternoon flew, and it was almost six by the time she got home. She had forgotten the troublesome tooth, and also her morning visitor by then, and Libby made no reminder of the little episode when she told Miranda there was a salad and some home-cooked pressed beef and a cherry pie ready for her whenever they were required.

After Libby had gone down to her own flat Miranda curled up on the wide settee to listen to her new records. She was not in the least lonely now, or forlorn at the thought of spending the evening in her own company. She was going to wash her hair, have a leisurely and luxurious soak and do her nails, then she was going to wait up for Jason, even if it was into the small hours before he returned. However, it was only a few minutes after ten, she was scarcely out of the bath and just completing a rather elaborate packaging in black and gilt paper of the present, when she heard the dull metallic sound of the garage door. She sped down the hallway to greet him, the chiffon folds of the midnight blue negligée floating out behind her.

There was a blustery wind rising, with flurries of rain on its wings, and he brought the cool damp of it in with him, on the soft smooth stuff of his jacket and on his cheek as she went into his arms.

'Warm and wanton – you'll get your death!' he exclaimed,

bussing her generously. 'Missed me as much as all that?'

'Shouldn't I?' She didn't wait for an answer to that and said happily: 'I'm glad you're not terribly late after all.'

He shot the bolts on the rear door. 'Our man was feeling a bit travel-weary, so the evening was cut to essential discussions. Had a good day?'

'Mm, super. I went shopping and bought you two gigantic presents – expense no object.' She rushed ahead of him into the lounge and thrust the two packages into his hands.

'It isn't my birthday, is it?'

'No – do you want anything to eat?'

'No, thanks.' He turned the black and gilt packages over in his hands, then sat down to open them.

'Shall I make you some coffee?'

He shook his head.

'A drink?' She hovered.

'No, thanks.'

'No?' She perched on the arm and watched him sniff the spicy tang of the toiletries. He glanced up, one brow quirked.

'Thank you – where's the guarantee?'

'What guarantee?'

'Aren't these the kind that guarantee to make a man utterly irresistible to all women? Will I cause havoc on the underground?'

'You rarely use the underground,' she said dryly.

He sat up straight. 'I must try them straight away. This minute.'

'In that case, as there's nothing I can get you . . .' Pretending indifference, she uncurled and stood up, knowing his mood and that his hand would close like a whiplash round her wrist, challenging her to escape.

It was all part of the game and the exhilaration of the desire he had taught her to kindle. His mouth curved as without scruple for his superior male strength he pulled her off balance and dragged her down into his arms.

His eyes sparkled with devilry. 'Maybe I said there was nothing you could get me – but I didn't say there was nothing you could give me.'

'Oh . . . I must have got the wrong impression.'

'That's your story . . . see it doesn't happen again.'

The flacon of bath oil rolled down on to the carpet and lay there, unheeded except for a small breathless exclamation from

Miranda, also unheeded.

She felt the velvet bandeau slide from her head under the domination of his hands. His fingers tangled in the silky tresses as his mouth explored the warm white skin of her throat.

'You smell of honey and nectar and warm girl,' he said huskily.

'I'm made of warm girl . . .' Dormant senses were waking to the clamour he rarely failed to evoke in her now and her arms tightened round the lean hard contours of his shoulders, communicating all the love she wanted to give. A sigh shuddered through him as he curved the pliant body more closely, his fingers raking the soft, newly washed hair until it lay in a disordered cloud over his arm. For a moment he gazed down at her, satisfaction darkening the grey gaze, and murmured thickly: 'I like making you look like an abandoned woman.'

'I feel like an abandoned woman . . .'

There was no response, except the kiss that crushed her own soft responsive sigh against his mouth.

Much later she lay in a pleasant state of semi-wakefulness, musing on the day that was now over, and the muted chimes of the hall clock played the hour of midnight, bringing her to full wakefulness. Suddenly she remembered, and stirred.

'Jason, are you still awake?'

'I wasn't, but I am now,' he murmured sleepily.

'I've just remembered—'

'True to form!' He rolled over and threw one arm across her, sighing. 'I wish you'd lose your memory at night. Is it vital?'

'No, at least it might be.' She twined her fingers in his. 'A woman called this morning – someone you know, darling. A Mrs. Lindsterne – Lissa. She—'

Jason's fingers had closed so sharply on hers she stopped.

'What did she want?' he demanded.

'To wish us happiness, and—' Miranda's shoulders moved in the semblance of a shrug – 'she and her husband had been on holiday. She's invited us to spend the week-end after next with them. I said – Jason! What's the matter? You're hurting my wrist.'

He turned away, yanking viciously at the bedclothes. 'You didn't accept, did you?'

'Well, yes . . .' Puzzled, she raised herself on one arm to stare down at the dark outline of his head. 'At least I said we'd go if you were free.'

'We're not,' he snapped, 'and in future ask me before you accept invitations from people you've never met.'

'But you do know them, don't you?' More puzzled than ever, she bit her lip. 'You were at Winchester with him, or so she said. Why are you angry?'

'I'm not angry.'

'I'm sorry.' Miranda sank back on the pillow. 'I thought she . . .'

'Oh, for God's sake, let's get to sleep. We'll have the inquest in the morning.' Savagely he pulled the sheet over his head and presented a hunched, uncompromisingly unfriendly back that defied the most placating of soft little arms to steal timidly across it.

Miranda knew Jason's moods too well by now to persist, and her mouth trembled as she hunched forlornly into a small lonely huddle at her own side of the bed. What on earth had she said? Or done? How was she to know he didn't like the Lindsternes? She'd taken Lissa Lindsterne on trust; what else could she have done?

Sleep retreated farther and farther away as she tried to work out why Jason was so angry, and presently the nagging ache concentrated itself in the most vulnerable spot, the troublesome tooth. She spent a sleepless night with toothache, not daring to get up and seek aspirins lest she disturbed Jason and incurred his further wrath. In the morning she was wan and melancholy, and Jason's dark countenance did not look encouraging.

His responses were terse and unfeeling at breakfast, and finally she gave up the pretence of pretending that nothing had happened and lapsed into miserable silence. It was not until he poured his second cup of coffee that he looked directly at her and said flatly: 'I'll cancel that invitation; you can forget it.'

'Whatever you want,' she said wearily. 'I don't care whether we go or not.'

For the first time he noticed the plate pushed aside unused. 'You haven't eaten anything,' he said sharply.

'I'm not hungry.' She evaded his eyes.

His brows drew together. 'Did you make that appointment, by the way?'

'No.'

His mouth tightened in a grimace of exasperation. 'Scared, I suppose. Listen, it's no use putting it off. I'll arrange for you to see my own man, today if possible. He's excellent, so you need have no qualms.'

'Yes, but not today – I'm going to the hairdresser,' she protested.

'Tomorrow, then.'

'I'm meeting Susan for lunch – I haven't seen her for ages.'

'For at least two weeks!' He gulped the remainder of his coffee and glanced at his watch. 'Which will bring us to the week-end. Oh no, Miranda, we're not having best part of another week of broken nights through toothache. It's so senseless to put up with pain which can be remedied.' He stood up. 'I'll ring you from the office at ten this morning and let you know when he can fit you in, then you'll have to juggle your other appointments to suit.'

The kiss he dropped on her cheek was a very brusque token as he told her he would be home early that evening. 'No joy,' she whispered to herself as he hurried out, leaving her to ponder anew on the cause of his irateness and hope that by the evening he might have relented.

But it proved a vain hope. Miss Mayo made the promised phone call to inform her that her dental appointment was fixed for the following afternoon at three-fifteen, and Jason landed home with a briefcase full of work, with which he disappeared into the study immediately after the evening meal.

He was a little more amiable, she was forced to admit, but the atmosphere of strain was still discernible and when he joined her shortly after nine he seemed disinclined for idle talk, and still less inclined to indulge in loveplay.

He did not mention the fateful invitation and she was still too unsure of him to raise the matter herself. Obviously something about the Lindsternes bothered him, or why should the mention of them destroy so quickly and utterly what had been a blissful interlude? She remembered the odd little tremors of unease as she went to greet her visitor, and that odd exchange of glances between Libby and the attractive newcomer. Imagination? Or a kind of premonition . . . ?

Of course it was imagination, she reasoned with herself as she got ready to meet Susan the following day. And it was ridiculous to imagine that there was a new barrier of restraint between herself and Jason . . . It was simply that he was irritable with overwork; he lived at too high a pressure. She must try to be patient and understanding. All the same, he might have been a little more patient and understanding over Lissa Lindsterne's innocent invitation. Full circle again! Determinedly she forced the circle of worry to break and began to run as she saw Susan peeping from the café entrance where they'd arranged to rendezvous.

It was the first time she'd been alone with Susan for a leisurely chat since her marriage and there seemed to be so many things she wanted to ask about her old office-mates.

'Everyone's asking after you,' Susan said, 'especially Rena Harvey – she's got a nerve!'

Miranda nodded. Her own memories of Rena were not exactly affable. 'Who's she lampooning now?' she asked.

'You may well ask.' Susan took a deep breath, but forbore to mention that it was Miranda herself who was still the cause of a great deal of speculation concerning her marriage to J.S., and Rena, in that coarse, blasée way of hers, had boldly given her estimate of how long the marriage would last. Two years at the most; more likely one, was her verdict, before J.S. wearied and sought more exciting diversions. But Susan had now suffered first-hand experience of Rena's particular attention and she was smarting with rage. She was also feeling a trifle guilty.

In sympathetic silence Miranda listened to the story of Rena's inquisitive sallies and insinuations regarding Susan and Ray. 'I told her to mind her own business,' she said furiously. 'As it happens, we don't, not yet, but it's no business of hers if we did. But I'm sure half the department believes that Ray and I have shacked up. Actually he wants us to get engaged. He's terribly serious, wants to save up the deposit for our own house – and you know what sort of money *that* takes. And he wants me to give up my job once we're married. But I'm not sure if I want to give up working. I like having my own money – I don't believe in a woman being completely dependent on her husband for every penny – it's Victorian.'

Miranda nodded. She knew that longing for independence. 'I should stall for a while if you're not sure,' she advised. 'But be honest with Ray. Tell him what you've told me.'

'Oh, I shall! But two years ... I might meet somebody else.'

'Well, better before marriage than after. That was the original idea of engagements. A sort of testing time to get to know one another more closely.'

Susan nodded, and for a little while the two girls were silent,

126

giving their attention to their lunch while they pondered. Susan finished her mushroom omelette first and looked up.

'I seem to have hogged the conversation.' Her eyes sparkled. 'How are you? Dare I ask what it's like living on the same plane as the great J.S.?'

'If I live long enough I may get used to it.' Miranda's eyes took on a misted faraway light as she realized she could never formulate the answer to Susan's question. 'But he's just insisted I go to the dentist and made the appointment himself to make sure I do,' she said ruefully. 'It's this afternoon, actually, but I've plenty of time, so we can take our time over lunch.'

'Poor you,' Susan shuddered. 'But you might have known he'd be the managing type. Are you truly happy?' she asked in a somewhat different tone.

'I think so,' Miranda said slowly. 'If I say that I couldn't visualize myself ever wanting any other man than Jason, would that give you the answer?'

Susan toyed with a knife, trying to balance it on its edge. When she set it straight and looked up there was a hint of guilt in her eyes and a certain awkwardness in her manner. 'I – I don't quite know how to say this,' she began slowly, 'but I must. I should never have repeated those things I told you that night before your wedding. But at the time I felt I had to tell you, warn you, in case it was true, because if afterwards . . .'

Miranda had gone white. 'What do you mean, afterwards?'

'Well, you could have been dreadfully unhappy and it would have been my fault. Because I thought it was true,' Susan hurried on, as though anxious to get it explained and over. 'Everybody knows that Rena and Money Travers are like that—' she held up two crossed fingers '—and he's very friendly with Mr. Ambrose, who was very friendly with Mr. Frears before he was moved to Rome. And Mr. Frears was—'

'Was very friendly with Jason until they both got involved with Catrina Kay. I know,' Miranda finished for her, 'but actually it was arranged for Mr. Frears to be transferred to Rome before it happened. He's coming back next month and we're having him to dinner one evening.'

'So Jason does talk about things to you?'

'Most things,' Miranda said after a brief hesitation. It was true; he did often tell her about his work and his colleagues, but it wouldn't be entirely true to say he confided in her about his past affairs. He had, however, remarked sardonically one day that he supposed she'd heard all about the Catrina Kay business, then added that the grapevine, though very efficient, wasn't one hundred per cent accurate. She said aloud: 'Jason would never allow personal affairs to influence his business actions. He did feel a bit annoyed about Mike at the time, but it had nothing to do with his transfer to Italy.' She hesitated. 'What are you trying to tell me, Sue?'

'Just that I'm sorry. It could have ruined everything for you, and I'm sure it was all exaggerated gossip. You see, Rena said you were just an innocent going in with your eyes shut, and somebody ought to give you a hint about the man you were going to marry.'

'Yes,' Miranda's lips set as she remembered the anguish of that long night, 'but I doubt if Rena knows the meaning of the word "trust". I chose to trust him, because I don't believe he would have given up his freedom if he'd wanted to go on from affair to affair. It didn't add up.'

'Oh, I agree!' Susan seemed relieved, for she laughed. 'I reckon old Rena was peeved because she wasn't the first to get to know. I told her off, you know, and she had the nerve to say there was no smoke without fire where a man like J.S. was concerned.'

Miranda took a gulp of her coffee and wished she could summon enough courage to ask Susan to change the subject. Part of her desperately wanted to hear whatever it was her friend was about to impart, the other self was more craven, dreading what it might hear. She said in a small choked voice: 'Really!' and tried to look blasée.

'Yes.' Susan rounded her eyes, as though to express her own fervent disapproval. 'But I insisted that she told me because I felt it was time to see if there were any actual facts behind dramatic hints she's always throwing out.' Susan took a deep breath and leaned forward. 'Apparently it started the night she went to the Lyric with a friend to see – I forget what she said the show was called, but it was the week when J.S. came back from Stockholm. Anyway, during the interval she and her friend went for a drink and who should they see but—'

'No!'

Miranda spoke so sharply that Susan jerked back.

'What's the matter?'

'Nothing. But I don't think I want to hear any more of Rena

Harvey's tales,' Miranda said firmly. 'I don't care who she saw my husband with at the theatre, and I don't want to discuss it any more. It's all over.'

'Yes, I know,' Susan protested, 'but I think you should know, just to straighten things out. That's why I—'

'There's nothing to straighten out. What Jason did before our marriage doesn't concern me, any more than my personal affairs before I met him. Please forget it.'

In silence Susan stared back. Miranda's face had lost some of its colour and her mouth was taut. Only her eyes betrayed the haunted shadows. Susan bit her lip. 'I – I'm sorry. I only—' She shook her head and gave an exclamation as her dinner napkin slipped to the floor. She bent to retrieve it and straightened to embarrassed silence. 'I – I think I'll have another cup of coffee,' she said at last.

Miranda reached for her cup and refilled it, her movements appearing more calm than her inward emotions warranted. 'When are you going on holiday?' she asked.

'In a fortnight's time.' Susan did not sound at all enthusiastic at the prospect and there was another awkward silence. Suddenly she looked appealingly at Miranda. 'Have you forgiven me?' she asked unhappily.

'What for?'

'You know what for.'

'Of course I've forgiven you – would I be having lunch with you today if I hadn't?' Miranda sighed. 'You did what you thought was best. Now please . . . let's forget it.'

Susan nodded, and to Miranda's relief relinquished the subject at last. Soon after that they parted: Susan to rush back to work, and Miranda to the unavoidable session that awaited her at the dentist's.

She was early for her appointment and settled herself in the silent, aseptic-smelling waiting-room, for once indifferent to a prospect that usually made her very faint-hearted indeed. What exactly had Susan tried to tell her? Had she discovered the facts behind that disturbing warning on her wedding eve?

She reached for a magazine, looked at it unseeingly, then laid it down again without opening its pages. She should have let Susan talk; perhaps it might have allayed some of her doubts, and Susan had protested that she wanted to clear things up. But what was there to clear up? It happened before our wedding, Miranda insisted to herself. There was probably a perfectly innocent explanation – always supposing that he had been seen with a married woman. *I must have trust*, she told herself, desperately trying to short-circuit the vain reiteration of the old argument. Resolutely she closed her mind to it all and selected a magazine from the assortment on the table.

She leafed through it steadily, skipping the centre gravure section devoted to society news and gossip. But somewhere in the blurred rush of print a certain name registered and made her search back until she located it. It was a half-page photograph of Catrina Kay, taken at a star-studded charity function held some time previously. Miranda looked curiously at the *gamin* features which must once have held Jason in such thrall, and then at the startlingly attractive man depicted with the starlet. His pale hair looked almost as brilliantly platinum as the shining locks of Catrina herself.

Miranda's mouth curved. Strangely she felt no pangs whatever of jealousy. Some instinct told her that Jason would scarcely register the fact were Catrina to walk by right under his nose. Then she read the caption and a cold shock gripped her. True to the style of the particular magazine, the caption gushed:

'*Off with the old! And our Trina's new affair – gorgeous Beau Blaze, the sensational new singing star. But the old love, pictured below left at an E.E.C. affair in Brussels, seemed unconcerned. And why should he be, with luscious Mrs. Alicia Lindsterne, deb-of-her-year, back in his arms? Carona-Steele's tough young titan isn't saying. But we can't help wondering: was the orchestra playing, 'Tis better to have loved and lost than never . . .?*'

Miranda almost dropped the magazine. *Lissa!* The lovely features were unmistakable. All the pieces began to fall into place. This was the girl they used to talk about. The debby type who'd turned him down . . . who'd married someone else, someone with rolling acres down in Hampshire . . . She was the source of the rumours avidly seized on by Rena Harvey . . . she was the married woman . . .

The sick aching fear rose in waves, leaving her numb while she fought to control the terrible suspicion. It couldn't be true. It was over. It had to be. It would be an old magazine – the date would prove it.

With nerveless fingers she sought the date on the cover. April 20th. It almost wasn't an old copy. Just a week after her marriage. But when had the photograph been taken? Didn't some magazines take weeks to go to press? But not all of them. It must have been taken before that momentous night when Jason proposed. It had to be. But Jason had proposed totally without warning. He could scarcely have known his own intention that night; if it hadn't been for giving her a lift, and going to sleep, and Mrs. Saunders turning awkward, maybe he would never have uttered those calm little words ... But Lissa ... did he still love her? Was this the explanation for his behaviour over her invitation this week ... *Oh, no!*

Miranda got up like an automaton and replaced the magazine. It stared back at her like an object of fate and she sank back into the chair, burying her face in her hands.

'Mrs. Steele.'

The receptionist's voice, a hint of impatience in it, came from a long way away. Miranda stood up on legs that trembled and took a step forward. The nurse-receptionist's expression changed and her voice took on a practised quality of soothing.

'There's no need to be nervous, now ...' She took Miranda's arm. 'Lots of patients are nervous the first time, but never the second, not here. Take my word for it. It'll probably only be a tiny filling, my dear.'

'I – I'm not nervous,' Miranda denied in a thin voice.

It was true now, but the older woman's smile was one of soothing disbelief.

Miranda emerged a little while later with a new filling in the troublesome tooth and a new ache elsewhere that would not be banished. The waiting-room was empty, and she did something that normally her honest soul would never permit. With a hasty glance round to make sure she was unobserved she stole the magazine and walked quickly out of the building.

CHAPTER TEN

THE glossy black and silver cover of that magazine haunted Miranda's waking moments during the weeks which followed, and every detail of the photograph on page thirty-seven was indelibly stamped on her mind. All the way home that afternoon she was resolved to ask Jason when he had last met Lissa, but when the moment came, when he inquired about the dental verdict she could find no words to frame the question. It should have been so easy simply to say lightly: 'There was a mag in the waiting-room – look,' and show him, then wait for his comment. But like a lot of things in theory, to put it into practice proved impossible.

She hid the magazine in her dressing table drawer, and tried to forget it existed. Common sense assured her that she had no reason to suspect Jason of being unfaithful and she would be foolish to allow suspicion to poison her marriage. But despite her attempts to make logic keep the darker emotions in check something had withered in the fragile new relationship that had scarcely begun to grow between herself and Jason. Often she thought of that happy evening which had ended so unhappily with her mention of Lissa's visit, and even though Lissa made no further personal contact, nor was she referred to again, her shadow was a tangible thing on Miranda's path. Sometimes she thought that Jason noticed the air of restraint, but he never commented, even though she knew she had lost the delightful spontaneity that had characterized her first tentative response to his lovemaking.

One morning in June he looked up from a letter he had singled out from the morning's personal mail and said suddenly: 'We need a break – and we've got to fit it in before this.' He passed the deckle-edge missive across the breakfast table.

She took it, and saw that it wasn't a letter but a silver engraved card. She scanned it, then gave a wondering exclamation. 'Their ruby wedding anniversary! That's forty, isn't it?'

Jason nodded. 'Our chairman and his lady have survived forty whole years of connubial bliss – I reckon they deserve a celebration.'

She pretended not to notice the cynical note in his voice. 'It's on the tenth of next month and we're invited. Oh, I hope you won't be away.'

'Not for this one – I wouldn't dare. I believe they're planning quite a do.' He reached for the toast and marmalade. 'They're praying for one of those fine warm summer evenings so that the celebration can flow out into the grounds. I believe the provisional programme is to start with cocktails and a formal dinner and the toasts, then a cabaret and dancing, followed by a midnight barbecue – weather permitting – and an informal free-for-all until the last guest is too weary to stay awake. So,'

Jason paused, then went on through a mouthful of toast, 'I thought we'd steal a break now in case I can't take it later.'

She nodded. 'You must have a break this year. You told me you haven't had a holiday for two years.'

He shrugged. 'I'm thinking of you mainly. Where would you like to go?'

'Anywhere.'

'Rather a broad choice in that helpful statement!'

'Well, I think it should be somewhere quiet,' she qualified.

'So do I. Abroad?'

'If you want to. Where do you want to go?' she asked seriously. 'It's as much your holiday as mine.'

'Well, I thought we might go to the Highlands. There's a lodge I borrow occasionally. It's private – on an estate – and overlooks the loch. There's a river close by and superb fishing, and no phone. One has to walk half a mile to the factor's house to use the phone, or drive several miles to the village. The scenery is out of this world, but when I say it's quiet I mean quiet. You might get bored after the first couple of days,' he warned.

Instinct told her that Jason needed this chance to unwind and she said firmly: 'It sounds perfect, and I've always wanted to go to the Highlands. Let's go there if you can fix it.'

'I can, provided it's this month. But he's letting the lodge to an American family during July and August, so it has to be now. Shall I fix it for Friday week?'

'Yes, please.' Suddenly she felt a warm rush of anticipation. It would be wonderful to get away from the pressure of city life and relax in the serenity of the countryside. 'Shall I tell Libby, so that she can cancel milk and things?'

'Yes, and will you send a formal acknowledgement of this, accepting?' He stood up, indicating the invitation as he did so. 'Incidentally, we'd better get the present one day this week. Any bright ideas?'

She hadn't, not at that moment, but a few days later they went shopping for this very special gift for Sir Charles and his lady. After much deliberation they chose a rare old Venetian goblet of rich ruby crystal. It cost the earth, so much that Miranda refused to carry it home, and Jason took charge of the precious package with a nonchalance that secretly appalled her, announcing that he would instruct the faithful Miss Mayo to deliver it personally to the chairman's home.

As the week drew to its close Miranda was possessed by a secret sense of anticipation and by the eve of the journey she was filled with excitement and feeling happier than she had felt for several weeks. The weather was warm and promising – almost too warm in London where the streets seemed airless and stifling – and the long range forecast predicted a heatwave.

They set off very early on the Friday morning, and crossed the Border with ample time to wend their way to the small country hotel where Jason was breaking the journey for the night.

The weather still kept its promise, staying dry, clear and sunny, showing the beautiful Scottish countryside to its fullest advantage as they wended their way north through the western approaches and on to Fort William, where they stopped to stock up provisions for the week-end. London seemed a thousand miles away beyond the blue-hazed mountains when at last Jason sighed and murmured: 'Nearly there.'

The sun had set and the crimson pearl was shading into night when Jason swung the car into the narrow turning under an avenue of oak and rowan, and some five miles further along the tortuous twists it widened into a small clearing, and there was the lodge.

The stillness was intense when the whine of the car engine ceased, and then she heard the gurgling music of a burn nearby. But they had failed to beat nightfall, and the irresistible beckoning sounds of a stream that seemed to say 'Come and find me', had to be resisted until morning.

There were the provisions to be carried in, the cases to unpack, the lodge to explore, and a meal to be fixed on a calor gas cooker. To say nothing of lamps to be lit!

'You didn't tell me there was no electricity,' she said with mock ruefulness.

'No, but I did warn you that you might be bored,' he retorted.

She shook her head, watching him examine fishing tackle that was sorted with scrupulous neatness along one wall of the lobby. 'You wanted to come here very much, didn't you?' she asked with a flash of perception. When he nodded she said lightly: 'You can teach me to fish – I've always wanted to.'

She wanted to believe that during those calm days she found a new camaraderie with Jason, one in which the frequent long silences were as companionable as the amusement her fishing efforts invoked in him. For the first three days they saw not another living soul apart from the factor, who called in on the Sunday to see if all were well with the visitors.

She forgot the crisp summery frocks she had brought and lived in an old pair of jeans and a checked shirt that really belonged to Jason. Far from being bored she found so much to explore and do that the days seemed to flash by. The burn was one of her favourite spots, just a short distance away. It was like crystal come to life as it tumbled joyously down its rock-rough bed, to a cascade feathered in fern and moss that fell to a wide pool in the cool green shadows of the forest. And the view of the loch that waited her eyes each morning on waking was her favourite subject for musing on, with elbows spread along the windowsill, until Jason demanded breakfast.

There was a small sandy beach from which they could swim, but she ventured in only once. Despite the warmth of the sun the water was glacial, and after that first icy experience she shed any thought of bravado and enjoyed lazy hours stretched out in the sun, watching the sun sparkles glissading over the water to the dark green firs on the far shore and the violet-misted majesty of the encircling mountains.

She had almost forgotten her doubts, and she had almost succeeded in banishing Lissa from her memory. When the first week ended she knew a genuine regret that only three days remained. Suddenly they became precious, to be hoarded and spun out to their fullest extent in the savouring of this frail contentment, one which she dared to believe Jason also shared. So when the last day dawned, hotter than ever, and they tacitly agreed to spend it lazily by the lakeside, she was a little surprised the moment when she looked up and discovered Jason surveying her bikini-clad form rather more than intently.

She took off her sunglasses. 'What's the matter?'

'Nothing, except ... He hesitated. 'You've seemed a bit withdrawn of late.'

'I haven't.' Her face puckered as she stared back.

'I don't mean here. I mean before we came away. Almost as though there was something bothering you.'

A whisper of breeze suddenly seemed cool on her skin. Slowly she replaced the shielding sun-shades. 'I don't think so,' she said uncertainly.

His head made one of those small sideways movements that express contradiction but also a disinclination to argue. He looked at the lake. 'I suppose you're not . . .'

The unfinished allusion failed to register. 'Not what?' she asked, her eyes puzzled.

He gave a lopsided grin and slapped her thigh lightly. 'What is fashionably known outside wedlock, I believe, as being in the club.'

'Oh.' She knew now and her expression betrayed her distaste. 'But we're not outside wedlock.'

He jutted his lower lip, then his own expression changed.

'I'm sorry, darling. But it did occur to me – although you shouldn't be,' he added dryly.

'I'm not going to have a baby, if that's what's worrying you,' she said flatly.

'It isn't worrying me!' He sighed impatiently. 'I'm trying to discover if anything is worrying *you*.'

A constriction caught at her, and she felt thin prickles of chill down her limbs, despite the hot sun. This was the perfect opportunity, at last. No risk of interruptions, no phone, no business to summon him away. She had his undivided attention and a wide open lead. This was the moment to sit up and say: *Yes, I'm worried, frightened, because you might be still in love with a girl called Lissa, because everything seems to point to your having an affair with her right till the eve of our marriage, may be still, for all I know, and because you've never yet told me in so many words that I matter to you more than any other woman in the world, and that your only reason for marrying me was because you loved me, not because you wanted me – for there's a difference – and not for some strange reason of your own which I've always sensed but never dared ask you to divulge . . .*

But her lips framed none of those questions which still tormented her whenever she failed to force them out of her mind. The truth was, she dared not. She still didn't know enough of the man who was her husband to predict the outcome.

He said suddenly, 'I suppose we should discuss the matter seriously one of these days.'

She was so far distant in her own train of thought that she stared at him, her eyes narrowed with query as much as with the bright sun.

'Do you want a family?' He betrayed impatience. 'Sometimes I can't read you at all. Are you a maternal kind of girl after all, I wonder?'

She was silent, and he went on musingly: 'I seem to remember; once you stated quite clearly that you wanted marriage, a home, and children – but you omitted the one vital factor usually associated with that particular combination.'

'Yes,' she sat up and folded her arms round her knees, 'I remember. You reminded me then of my omission.'

'Naturally.' He stretched lazily and lay back, making his hands into a pillow for his head. 'But you haven't answered my question, Miranda.'

She looked down at his tanned body, broad and muscular before it tapered down to narrow hips in the dark blue swim slips. She bit her lip as her glance moved to the enigmatic line of his mouth.

'Do *you* want children?' she asked.

He hesitated, then turned his head. 'I'd like a son, and then a daughter.'

'So would I, I think,' she said slowly.

'But not for a while,' he said, his gaze turning towards her, caressing her with its sudden flicker of awakening desire before he reached up towards her. 'I want to get used to the state of marriage before I face fatherhood . . .'

The words, although spoken without any trace of cynicism, nevertheless inflicted a small chill, and she did not realize how deeply she sighed as she went into his arms . . .

*   *   *

There was the usual accumulation of what Jason called 'Bumph' waiting on their return home. But among the circulars, the holiday postcards from vividly-hued faraway places, and persuasively worded offers of never-to-be-repeated-again bargains was a letter for Miranda.

She scanned the closely written sheet, and a smile curved her mouth. Jason noticed it and raised his brows. 'It's not a bill, anyway.'

'No – it's from Mrs. Gordon. Did I ever tell you about her?' Miranda looked up. 'She used to be my aunt's daily help, and rather a darling. I sent her a piece of wedding cake and a short note and I was beginning to think she hadn't received it. But she's been away,' Miranda returned her attention to the copious flow in Mrs. Gordon's favourite purple ink, 'and just got back last week. She'd been nursing her widowed sister who's had an operation . . .' Miranda stopped, and read on in silence – Jason would not be interested in the rather revolting details of Mrs. Gordon's unfortunate sister's operation. 'Oh, she got a terrific surprise when she heard I was married and she sends her very best wishes for our happiness and says she can't quite believe it – it seems no time since she was chasing me out to catch the bus for school . . .'

Miranda glanced up again, to discover that Jason had returned his attention to the *Telegraph* and she was talking to the air. But the musing smile of retrospect still played about her mouth.

How far away those days at Evesham seemed now. Almost as though they belonged to another age. Yet all less than seven months ago. If she had dithered, played safe by staying in the homeland she'd always known, she wouldn't be sitting here, looking at the darkly etched profile of her husband above the newspaper. As though he felt her regard he closed the paper and sent her an inquiring glance.

She put the letter down. 'I'll have to make arrangements about my things. Mrs—'

'What things?' He frowned.

'Remember? Some furniture and—'

He nodded quickly. 'You want to bring them here?'

'Yes, because Mrs. Gordon wants to have her sister come and live with her, because of her sister's poor health, and she needs the room.'

'Well, what's the problem?' Jason asked. 'We've plenty of spare room upstairs for your childhood treasures,' he grinned, 'if you don't want to part with them. And we can probably find homes for the other items.'

She hesitated, her brow serious. 'Actually, I've been wondering about that. I can't visualize Aunt Hester's stuff fitting in here. It's all cottagey style – you know, old oak mostly. Although there's a beautiful little satinwood side table that would go in that alcove on the first landing. But Mrs. Gordon says the man in the post office is very interested and she's to let him have first chance if I want to sell the stuff.'

'Oh, he does, does he?' Jason folded the paper. 'You'll sell nothing till I've had a look at it. We'd better go down at the first opportunity. Some of it may be extremely valuable.'

How quickly he reverted to businesslike practicality, she thought. Two days later they drove to Evesham, lunched there, and drove out to Upper Mingbury to the home of the suddenly emotional Mrs. Gordon.

When the initial excitement of the reunion abated she showed Jason the well-loved pieces she had been reluctant to let go and he announced that he would arrange for a carrier to pick up the larger items and in the meantime they could take the small stuff that afternoon as there was ample space in the car.

They had to stay to tea, after which they loaded the car, and it seemed the entire village already knew that Hester Grey's niece was back, with her husband. Smiles and waves came over the neat hedge, and from the gardens across the street, and when Jason drove off he remarked dryly: 'Now I know what running the gauntlet means. Villagers!'

'Everyone knew my aunt. She lived here all her life,' Miranda told him. 'I suppose I should have called on a few people.'

'Why didn't you say so?'

'And dragged you round a lot of strange houses?' She was surprised. 'You'd have been bored, so I didn't suggest it.'

'Me? I'd have let Mrs. Gordon entertain me for an hour. She's quite an indomitable character, and I think she was disappointed we didn't stay longer – she wanted to weigh me up and find out if I'm good for you,' he added sardonically.

'Wouldn't I be the one to supply that information?'

'You?' His mouth curved at one corner. 'Since when did any woman know when she was well off?'

'The moment she wasn't.' Miranda settled back to watch the countryside speed by, whisking away the miles to town. The visit to her old home had been all the more joyful for being planned unexpectedly, and the warmth of Jason's teasing mood added a poignant note to her day's happiness.

But it was to be tinged by disappointment when they got back that evening and he broke the news that he would be away the following week.

'Oh no! Not again!'

'Oh yes! And I can't say I'm exactly looking forward to it myself,' he said brusquely. 'Rome will be like a blast furnace if this weather continues.'

'Yes.' She glanced out of the window at the fiery sunset that promised to tint the clouds with shepherd's delight, that old countryman's portent for yet another fine day. 'How long?' she sighed.

'Two days Rome. Two days Bonn,' he said laconically.

There was a silence, then he moved to her side and dropped one hand on her shoulder.

'Why don't you go down to the cottage for the week?' he suggested. 'Get out of London for a change.'

'We've just come back,' she reminded him.

He shrugged. 'It seems years away already.'

It was true, she reflected. Already those idyllic ten days had receded into the past, their memory enclosed like a distant island.

'Alone?' she murmured doubtfully.

He shrugged. 'Take Libby. She'll look after you, and if I can I'll join you as soon as I get back.'

Abruptly his manner became brisk. 'I've just thought . . . your aunt's stuff would be ideal down there. I'll contact the carrier first thing in the morning and arrange to have it delivered there instead of here. But you'll have to be there that day – then you and Libby can amuse yourselves changing things round. Okay?'

She murmured assent, but the hint of doubt remained in her expression. 'Supposing I do take Libby, though, and you get back sooner than you expect – who'll look after you?'

'Me?' He laughed shortly. 'I'm not *that* helpless, darling.'

And so it was arranged. The carrier was to collect the things from Mrs. Gordon on the following Wednesday morning and deliver it at the cottage 'some time later' the same day.

Jason was leaving on the ten o'clock flight on the Monday morning, and at first he suggested rather peremptorily that Miranda and Libby should leave for Hampshire on the Sunday, when he would drive them down himself. But Miranda refused. She would see him off, then travel down by train after lunch. His attitude to this statement plainly betrayed that he considered it foolish whimsy, but he did not argue, and, encouraged by this, she announced she would see him off at the airport.

To this, however, Jason did take exception.

She listened, then said calmly: 'I know. You have this thing about not being seen off or met at airports. But please, just for once, let me satisfy my desire to wave my husband safe journey – and wish you luck and tell you to take care of yourself, like most wives do,' she pleaded a little breathlessly. 'And after this I'll try to content myself with watching you vanish across the square and waiting for the phone to ring telling me you're on your way home.'

'All right,' he sighed, 'but it still seems so pointless to me. All for the sake of a sentimental embrace with a mob of all nations milling around. If you could drive the car it would be different, but you'll have to come back under your own steam. Is it worth it?'

'I think so,' she said firmly. 'Please . . . ?'

'Have it your own way!' He gave her a crooked grin and upturned his palms; his way, she knew by now, of saying: the matter is closed.

She won her sentimental embrace, said those tender little wifely things she longed to say, and a little while later watched the plane take off. But by then the twin agonies of doubt and fear had captured her heart once more.

For, seemingly unnoticed by Jason while he waited, and in their turn apparently oblivious to his presence, two women stood talking animatedly to one another not so far from where Miranda and Jason waited. The Rome flight was called, and the younger woman kissed the older one and made off into the stream of departing travellers.

It was Lissa.

CHAPTER ELEVEN

As she watched the plane soar up into the white clouds Miranda tried to convince herself she had made a mistake. She had only met Lissa once, and she had seen her only in profile and then from behind in those moments before the flight was called. It could have been someone very like her . . .

But she knew in her heart she had made no mistake, and when, as she was leaving the building, she saw Lissa's companion it had the effect of destroying the frail attempt at self-delusion. She could not help staring at the older woman, wondering who she was, and noticed that she had lost the rather brittle air of animation that had been present when she talked to Lissa. The woman turned her head suddenly and met Miranda's gaze, and Miranda moved on hurriedly, conscious of the embarrassment of being caught staring, but not before she had recognized the likeness in features etched more strongly by maturity and realized that the other woman could be none other than Lissa's mother.

And Lissa was on that plane, even now was in the same section as Jason, perhaps talking to him, sharing a drink with him, arranging to meet in Rome, *if it all hadn't been arranged already* ...

Sick at heart, she recoiled from the ugly suspicion. Lissa might not be bound for Rome; she could be going to Paris, or ... Feverishly Miranda wished she had scanned the timetables to see if it was a direct flight – but Jason invariably endeavoured to take a direct flight; time was a vital commodity to him.

She was wan and preoccupied during the train journey to Hampshire that afternoon, unable to forget the slender graceful girl in pale green linen walking ahead of Jason's tall, dark-clad figure and hating herself for being unable to banish her fears. Desperately she clung to the thought that he would telephone her at night and the sound of his voice would bring the magic of reassurance. But as the hours passed and the phone stayed silent she was denied that longed-for consolation.

The days ahead seemed to stretch like an eternity. Because of Libby's presence she was forced to assume an air of normality she was far from feeling, and several times she wished she had insisted on Libby remaining at Byrne Square. Alone, she could abandon pretence while she existed through the long empty days, but not under Libby's shrewd and practical survey. There was also something she wanted to do, an idea that had flashed into her worried brain during the journey down, but one that she could not carry out when there was a chance of Libby overhearing.

It wasn't until the Wednesday morning when Libby announced she was going to walk down to the village to collect bread and a few oddments that Miranda had the opportunity of half an hour free from interruption.

She watched Libby set off with the shopping basket and round the bend of the lane before she took the card out of her handbag and sat down by the phone. For a moment she looked at the printed name and address, and the small note in Lissa's neat writing which added a second number – *'My mother's home number'*, and heard the echoes of Lissa explaining that she could be reached there when she was in town, which was quite often.

After a long hesitation Miranda dialled the Hampshire number, and found she was shivering while she waited for the dialling notes to cease abruptly with response from the other end. When it came, sooner than she expected, she couldn't make her voice frame a calm reply instantly.

The male voice at the other end of the line repeated rather testily: 'Yes, Lindsterne here. Speak up, please.'

She had a wild impulse to put down the receiver without answering. She resisted it and said unevenly: 'Could I speak to Mrs. Lindsterne, please?'

'I'm afraid you can't. She's in Rome.' The voice changed perceptibly, losing the tone of anonymity and gaining a trace of curiosity. 'Can I help?'

Miranda's throat tightened and the familiar chill settled in the pit of her stomach. 'No,' she managed, 'it isn't important at all. I'm sorry to bother you, Mr. Lindsterne.'

'Not at all. Lissa rushed off on Monday – Claire's been feeling under the weather lately, first baby coming and all that, and the heat's pretty atrocious just now.' He paused. 'I'm afraid I don't recognize your voice – should I be able to?'

'No, we haven't met.' Miranda swallowed hard and wished she hadn't started this; there was nothing now but to introduce herself.

For a moment there was a silence, then a surprised exclamation. He made the conventional responses, then went on: 'I'm sorry you couldn't make it that week-end. We were looking forward to meeting Jason's wife – still are, of course. But it takes a while to settle down and get acquainted with each other's crowd.'

He was talking pleasantly and easily now, the first trace of irritability gone. She tried to picture him, imagining him as a country type, more at home with dogs and a gun and the wind in his face than with the hothouse set or the arto-intellecto trend followers. Suddenly she wondered if he suffered the same agonizing uncertainties as herself. Was he ever tormented by the suspicion that his beautiful wife might regret turning down his best friend in favour of himself when she chose her marriage partner? Did he torture himself wondering if the old love affair had never really ended . . .? Suddenly she became aware of him saying: 'But you wanted to talk to Lissa . . . I don't know when she'll be back, but is there any message?'

With another stab of dismay she wished she had prepared a valid excuse for calling. She stammered, 'No, it was just that she left me her number and I just decided to ring . . .'

'Glad you did,' he said heartily.

In a moment he would suggest a visit as soon as it could be arranged, and she wondered how she could stall for time while she prayed Jason wouldn't get to hear of it. With the next breath James Lindsterne was doing exactly as she feared, but luck was on her side. Some sound must have disturbed him, for he broke off and remembered that he'd left the garden door open and the dogs would be rampaging in the kitchen.

'I must go and hoof them out,' he said quickly, 'but we're bound to meet at the Hubards' celebration next week and we can arrange something then. Lissa will be delighted.' With an apology he rang off, and she stared at the phone for some moments before she put it back on the rest.

'And he'll let out that I telephoned him,' she murmured distractedly, remembering the result of her first and only contact with Lissa Lindsterne. Had Jason's anger that night been born of guilt? There seemed no other logical explanation.

Listlessly she wandered out into the heat-laden garden. The fears that subterfuge invariably brings in its train paled quickly beside the certain knowledge she now possessed. Lissa was in Rome; Jason was in Rome; neither could fail to be aware that the other was present also. Even if they were lovers no longer some intangible thing remained to be resolved between them; until it was resolved there could be no peace of mind for Miranda, nor in her marriage.

She lived through those days in an agony of dread, made more frightening by the fact that Jason failed to telephone. In a half-hearted way she helped Libby to polish everything in the cottage and find new homes for the familiar treasures that the van delivered late on the Wednesday afternoon. On the Friday the heatwave broke with a violent thunderstorm, and in torrential rain Jason drove down to arrive without warning at ten o'clock that night.

His greeting was brusque and he made no attempt to embrace her when she ran to the door, surprise parting her lips. His thin jacket was soaked in the short journey to bring in his case and lock the garage door, and it was Libby who exclaimed suddenly:

'Are you all right, sir?'

With a sense of shock Miranda forgot her personal feelings and saw the drawn, shadowy hollows in his face and the pallor beneath his tan.

'Jason, what's the matter?' she cried.

144

'Nothing. I'm all right, just dead tired.'

'You don't look all right.'

'Don't fuss – I'll be okay by tomorrow.' He avoided her searching gaze and shrugged out of the wet jacket.

'What will you have?' Libby hovered by the door, ready for flight kitchenwards. 'There's some cold fresh salmon – I was going to do a mousse for tomorrow. Or I could grill a cutlet – it wouldn't take long – and there's raspberry crumble.'

Jason gave a visible shudder. 'Nothing, Libby. I'm not hungry. I—'

'Did you have something before you came down?' Miranda interrupted.

'I've scarcely eaten for two days.' He raked a hand through his damp hair and reached for his case, turning towards the stairs. 'Something I ate, probably.' Without a glance at the two alarmed faces upturned to him he went wearily upstairs.

Miranda looked at Libby, and the older woman shook her head. 'It's not use forcing food on him if he's had a gastric upset,' she counselled, 'but you should persuade him to take plenty of fluid, Mrs. Steele. Shall I mix some fruit juice and soda water?'

'Yes – no, I'll do it myself,' Miranda decided.

While Libby watched anxiously she filled a jug with orange juice diluted with soda water and put it on a tray with a glass. She hurried upstairs, to find the main bedroom empty.

There were four bedrooms in the cottage, one an airy, spacious room, two somewhat smaller, and a fourth that was little more than a box room. It was uneven in shape, tucked partly under the overhang of the thatch with a tiny dormer window, and, because it faced south, trapped and held a great deal of heat during warm weather. It was here that she found Jason, his things spread haphazardly over the bed and tiny chest of drawers, and the half-unpacked suitcase on the floor.

She stared at him in the shadowy light of the small lamp, her expression incredulous.

'Don't look so aghast.' He shrugged into his pyjama jacket and turned the bedcovers back. 'I'm going to spare you a disturbed sleep.'

He took the glass from the tray she still held and tipped the jug towards the light. 'What's this?'

'Orange and soda – but, Jason—'

'It's warmer in here as well.' There was a small bottle of

tablets on the ladderback chair by the bed, and he took two, gulping a mouthful of the orange juice.

'What are those?' She started forward.

'Antibiotics.'

Alarm began to flare. She looked round for somewhere to set the tray and seeing no space in the small room bent impatiently and put it on the floor. 'You can't sleep in here,' she protested, 'and you should have the doctor if you—' She reached out to place her hand on his brow and found it hot and damp. 'You've got a temperature,' she exclaimed. 'I think we should call the doctor.'

'I called a doctor in Rome – I never got to Bonn.' He sank down on the bed and swung his legs under the covers. 'Now don't fuss. The worst's over.'

'What do you expect me do? Not bother? Oh, Jason, you can't stay here. Please be sensible,' she pleaded. 'It's hot and airless, and not very comfortable.'

'Trying to tempt me?' A ghost of his old challenge glimmered in his eyes. 'Not tonight, Josephine, I'm afraid.'

She flushed scarlet. 'I wasn't thinking of that.' Almost angrily she began to snatch up the articles of clothing strewn round the room and fold them neatly. This again was untypical of him; normally he was extremely fastidious over personal tidiness, and she had never known him toss a jacket down into an open suitcase wherein sundry toilet accessories spilled from their waterproof holder. She rescued the jacket, tried to shake out the damp creases it had already gathered, and heard him murmur:

'I know you weren't.' He sighed, and the brief flare of spirit went out of his voice. 'Now don't worry, I'll survive. Just leave me and go and get your own sleep.'

'No. I'm staying here,' she said firmly, 'to make sure you're all right.'

His shoulders moved indifferently, and he turned away from the light. 'There's no need, but anything for peace . . .'

For a moment she stood there, watching him hunch down under the clothes, then she picked up the tray and went downstairs to recount her worries to Libby.

'I've only once known him ill during the years I've worked for him,' Libby said reminiscently. 'He had a cartilage operation on his knee. Put an end to his rugger capers. But he wasn't so much ill then as forced to give in until the trouble was put right. I shouldn't worry too much, it's probably just a stomach upset – too much rich food at all these business dinners,' she added flatly.

Miranda nodded, but she wasn't too sure about Libby's surmise. She made herself a cup of coffee, undressed and donned a housecoat, and made a fresh lot of fruit juice and soda. It was just as well that she did, for when she went quietly into the little bedroom she found him asleep and the first jug quite empty.

Libby had found some nightlights, packed away with candles and an oil lamp in one of the downstairs store cupboards, and Miranda settled herself with the tiny illumination where it would not disturb the sleeper. He did not sleep very long, and long before the night was over she suspected that Jason was more ill than he admitted. He was very restless, at one time requesting another blanket, and then a little while later pushing the clothes away as though he couldn't bear their warmth. He drank thirstily each time he awakened, complained once that he felt as though he'd been kicked by a mule, and told her three times to get some rest herself.

The following morning he got up, bathed and shaved as usual, but refused food all day and admitted to a raging headache. It was not until the Sunday that he began to look slightly less drawn and ate a little toast at a very late breakfast. During the afternoon he showed further signs of returning to normality when he perused the financial sections of the Sunday heavies and made a lengthy phone call to Sir Charles. When it was over he came back into the lounge and flopped down on the settee with his feet on the arm.

'Sir Charles sends his regards,' he said, 'and reminds us about the do next Saturday.'

She nodded, concern keeping her alert for any sign of the fever flaring again. He caught the intent regard, and his mouth curved with sardonic humour.

'You're looking a trifle wan yourself – you know now why I tried to warn you. Poor Miranda, you haven't had a very restful week-end, either.'

She shrugged, and the humour continued to play round his mouth.

'I've always endeavoured to keep out of the way of my women during the odd occasions I've fallen victim to blight. Sort of preserving the illusions,' he added cynically.

'But I'm not one of your women,' she reminded him gently. 'At least, I hope not.'

'Had enough already?'

She wished she could learn to ignore these moments when he reverted back to the rakish J.S. she had first known. But that was the Jason you fell in love with, she reminded herself, trying to mitigate the hurt to which that love was making her increasingly vulnerable. For she could not help but reflect on the way he had tried to shut himself away from her during his brief illness, which, even though it had not proved serious, had had a totally opposite effect on her, in that it instantly awakened in her the natural desire to care for him. But he had seemed not to want her gentle ministrations. She sighed softly, remembering his remark that day by the loch, when he told her he wanted to get used to the state of marriage before he embarked on the state of fatherhood.

She picked up one of the papers which had slid to the floor and curled up in the armchair, pretending to immerse herself in newsprint, as he was doing. But behind the shield of pages her expression grew troubled. How long before she and Jason attained that sense of oneness, for which she instinctively groped, believing it to be the true essence of a perfect relationship, of marriage . . .?

*   *   *

They returned to Byrne Square the following morning and Jason departed again almost immediately for the office. He seemed quite recovered, apart from the slightly drawn look still taut over his cheekbones and the loss of several pounds of weight, about which he was unconcerned, and she was aware again of that well-spring of vitality in him, the source of the power so characteristic in his personality.

He reminded her casually that evening about the special engagement at the week-end, asking her if she'd decided what to wear, and instantly she remembered.

Her concern over his illness had temporarily banished the other worry, but now all the misgivings rushed back in full spate. For the hundredth time she wished she'd spoken outright that day at the airport, pointing out the presence of the girl who had once played so important a part in his life. He would have been forced to make some comment, and at least the matter would have been brought into the open. But she had lacked the courage, and now it was too late.

Each day she was tense, half expecting Lissa to telephone or call. For surely she must know that Jason became ill in Rome. Unless she was still there. But James Lindsterne had made it quite clear that he and his wife would be at the Hubards' ruby wedding celebration.

Suddenly Miranda was dreading it.

But there was no phone call, and the Saturday dawned to clear skies and a soft stillness on the air which augured a perfect day. That evening she donned the new white dress of sheer silk jersey and long clinging lines that moulded her supple body to perfection. She raised her hands to her hair, the flowing mediaeval sleeves adding further grace to the movement, and encountered Jason's eyes through the mirror.

'Thank heaven,' he murmured dryly. 'I was afraid you might change your mind.' He held out a flat jeweller's box. 'I got this yesterday afternoon, but knowing women I was quite prepared to find you'd decided at the last minute to wear something different.'

He opened the box and moments later was fastening about her throat a heavy silver chain and pendant in the form of a Celtic cross. It was of antique silver, finely chased, and set with a circle of glowing garnets around the beautiful turquoise at its heart. Before she even glimpsed it through the mirror she knew that once again Jason had demonstrated his perfect taste and his knowledge of feminine adornment. The cross was an ideal complement to her gown and the plain, severely drawn back hair-style she had chosen.

He looked at her over her shoulder, then turned her away from the mirror so that she faced him. He nodded. 'Yes, I think so, don't you?'

She inclined her head, suddenly ashamed of all the doubts and suspicions she had harboured those past few days.

'It's beautiful – thank you. You spoil me, Jason.' Tremulously she looked up at him, and impulsively offered her lips.

He drew her towards him, then checked. 'Better not – I might ruin your make-up – it takes long enough to put on!'

She wanted to cry: *To pot with my make-up – I want to kiss you!* then the impulse died as she read the expression in his eyes. Undoubtedly they held appreciation of her appearance, but they also held the pride of possession. She remembered that there would be some two hundred guests at tonight's celebration, that among them would be some of the wealthiest in the land, people whom it was unlikely she would have met had she stayed in her own quiet, friendly country circle and never comes to the capital to meet and marry Jason Steele.

As though he read her thoughts he said: 'You're not nervous, are you?'

'Should I be?' she returned steadily.

'You've absolutely no cause to be,' he said crisply, 'but there'll be quite a few autocratic old dowagers there tonight, and a newcomer to their scene is often a subject of curiosity — not always the benign variety, either.'

'I shall have to remain at a discreet distance, then, won't I?' she said evenly, 'and make sure I don't disgrace you.'

'Little idiot!' he exclaimed with some vehemence, 'I'm trying to warn you — and protect you. The sheltered kind of upbringing you seem to have had provides little protection against the bitchery of high society.'

'There's bitchery in all society, at whatever level you try to categorize it.' She added the final touches of scent to pulse spots with a calmness of manner she did not feel and swung round to face him. 'You're making me nervous, Jason. Of whom have I to be afraid tonight?'

'I can't answer that because I don't know. Perhaps only yourself,' he said strangely, then glanced abruptly at his watch. 'Come on, we don't want to be too late.'

He was silent most of the drive to Maidenhead, where Sir Charles and Lady Hubard had their home in a gracious, rambling old mansion overlooking the river, and again Miranda felt the stir of foreboding. She wondered feverishly just what he had tried to warn her against, and decided sceptically that it was not the reason he had put into actual words. The only possible reason could be that of Lissa's presence — what else could it be? By the time Jason turned the car into the drive entrance she was chill with nerves and almost wishing the evening was over.

The wide tree-lined drive was already lined with parked cars, and at the curve half-way along they caught up with the tail of a line of slow-moving cars. At the head of the drive a manservant was directing the vehicles.

Jason stopped the car. 'You'd better get out and wait for me inside.'

She wanted to protest, to say that she didn't mind walking back from wherever Jason had to park the car, but the manservant was standing by the side of the car, and other cars were drawing up at the rear. She got out, holding the fullness of her white skirt lest it got marked, and went slowly up the three stone steps to the open door. Light, music and voices spilled out with that indefinable air of special celebration, and through open doors at each side of the spacious hall she saw people mingling, calling excited recognitions, and servants unobtrusively busy. The smell of opulence was all around, in light furs carried carelessly over bare arms – the evening was still pleasantly warm – elegant gowns, the sparkling battery of brilliance from jewel-swathed throats and bosoms, the high languid voices, the worldly assurance of the men, and the wafts of exclusive perfumes in blatant competition with one another.

Miranda looked round. There didn't seem to be a soul she knew, and she clutched the jewelled cross at her throat as though it were a talisman. In the moment while she wondered if she should move forward a voice spoke at her side and Lady Hubard was taking her hands and greeting her warmly.

'Now would you like to leave your wrap, my dear, while you wait for Jason – such a tiresome business tucking the car somewhere until it's wanted again.' She smiled and beckoned to an elderly maid hovering nearby. 'Marie will look after you – oh, and thank you so much for your beautiful gift. We will always treasure it,' she added. 'Charles and I are positively crazy over our collection of Venetian glass.'

What a marvellous memory, Miranda reflected as she followed Marie to the room which had been set aside for the ladies to leave their wraps in. Lady Hubard and her husband must have had well over a hundred gifts and yet she could remember instantly who had given what.

After depositing her light wrap and making an anxious check of her appearance she found her way back downstairs and saw Jason in an animated group near the foot of the stairs. He put out his hand, drawing her into the circle in the way that made her heart leap with the love he had evoked in her, and procured a drink for her. People were still arriving, and Sir Charles was greeting the new arrivals, jovially informing everyone that informality was the order of the evening.

'All we ask,' he declaimed, 'is that you wend your ways into the dining-room at eight o'clock. Afterwards my niece is going to dance for us – I'm not sure whether we should give her anything to eat! What do you think?' He put his arm round the shoulders of a slender, elfin child of about twelve and looked inquiringly at the guests.

'Shame,' said someone, and the elfin child dimpled mischievously at her uncle.

She was one of several children present, and as the guests began to move into the big dining-room, seeking their place cards and being guided by catering hostesses specially engaged for the occasion, Miranda saw more people whom she had met since her marriage. There was no sign of Lissa and her husband, and when the entire party was assembled at the long horseshoe table there were occasional gaps, almost inevitable with so large a guest list. Almost ashamed of the growing relief that was relaxing tension and bringing a joyous sense of integration with the festivities, Miranda appreciated the exquisitely decorated table. The main motifs were pink and silver, masses of tiny roses cascading from candelabra, silver twisted candles, silver lustre dinner ware, and a series of miniature fountains playing in which pink blossoms floated. The toasts brought the poignancy of sentiment into many hearts and there were the sounds of many throats being unashamedly cleared when the toastmaster finished his well-chosen words and the company raised their glasses to their hosts.

When the noise of chatter broke into the silence afterwards Wally Ambrose, who was on Miranda's left, nudged her and said mischievously:

'Wait for the day when *you* two are forty years on.'

Miranda shook her head. She couldn't imagine it at all. Jason turned his head inquiringly, and again she shook her head, whereupon Wally obligingly repeated his remark. Jason's mouth curved down at the corners. 'I'm not sure my wife's patience will last forty years,' he said dryly, and Wally chuckled.

'It's a virtue I haven't particularly noticed in you, my boy. Maybe you should—'

Miranda did not hear the rest of his chaffing remark. The double doors at the end of the long room had opened and two people entered. Lady Hubard had left her place and was going to greet them, concern in her face, and then murmuring to one of the waiters who escorted the newcomers to their places. The commiserations passed along the tables almost instantly: 'Cars!

Always break down at the most crucial times! Ghastly nuisance! Still, they got here!'

Lissa and James had arrived.

She looked more beautiful than Miranda remembered, even though traces of annoyance still marred her almost flawless features. She and James were placed on the other curve of the horseshoe table, out of range of Miranda's vision, but as soon as the meal was ended and the replete guests began a somewhat languid amble from the scene of eating she threaded her way deliberately towards Jason.

She flashed a brilliant smile of greeting at Miranda, then turned it on Jason. 'Are you quite recovered, Jason?'

He nodded, his eyes enigmatic. 'I'm fine, thank you.' He turned, obviously with the intention of introducing James Lindsterne who was just catching up with his wife, to Miranda, but Lissa forestalled him. She made the briefest of introductions, then went on: 'You had me really worried that evening you and Mike dined with us. I do believe' – she gestured artlessly – 'that if I hadn't insisted on calling Claire's doctor you'd have gone off to Bonn next morning and probably collapsed.'

Miranda was silent. She could not look at Jason. All she could think was that Jason hadn't told her . . .

'What's this? Who's collapsing?'

Wally Ambrose had joined the group in the doorway and had to be told.

'Jason? But he's indestructible,' Wally chortled.

'Famous last words,' said James Lindsterne.

'We're in the way here,' Jason reminded them, as the catering staff moved into the dining-room to clear away the tables and chairs.

Lissa dismissed this with a careless gesture, sidestepping gracefully as someone passed. 'Oh, have you seen the presents? We must go and see the presents.'

'They're in the morning-room,' said Jason, his hand touching the centre of Miranda's back.

Automatically she moved forward, into a general drift towards the morning-room where a tremendous array of gifts marking a great milestone in a marriage was displayed.

But Miranda hardly took in what she was seeing, even as her lips formed appropriate murmurs of admiration. Why hadn't he told her? Desperately she tried to persuade herself that it hadn't been important enough to him, that the fact of Lissa's making no secret whatsoever of the meeting should confirm this, but the effort was not successful. She looked at him now, seeking to read an answer, but Jason had donned his suave, polished party style and its façade was unassailable.

Lissa was openly envious of an exquisitely carved bowl of translucent green jade.

'Chinese, I'm sure. I hope you're not breaking the tenth commandment, Jason,' she teased.

'I leave that sin to the feminine sex,' he retaliated dryly.

Wally chuckled, and James Lindsterne remarked: 'I hope they've got this lot well insured.'

'We have,' Lady Hubard's sweet voice broke in. 'Now can I tear you all away? Diane is going to make her little contribution to the occasion and she'll be so disappointed if I don't round up an audience for her. After that I promise you there'll be no more organization,' she smiled, shepherding them firmly away. 'There'll be dancing and a cabaret later and the midnight barbecue for the youngsters, but we want you all just to make free of the place – wander down to the river if you want air – and just enjoy yourselves.'

She hurried off breathlessly to 'round up' more guests, and presently they found themselves in the big drawing-room where chairs had been arranged in semicircles at one end and lights grouped at the other end to provide as much illumination as possible. A young man sat at the Steinway grand, and in a little while he began to play and Diane made her appearance.

In a sugar-pink tutu she danced a gay variation from *Coppélia*, and while her technique *sur les pointes* occasionally betrayed traces of immaturity in artistry she showed the promise of the talented dancer she would become when her training was completed. After an item from the pianist she returned, this time in a clinging blue dress slit to the thigh, to interpret a sophisticated American blues number in a much more modern dance idiom.

There was nothing of polite indulgence in the applause which followed, and Wally Ambrose said with speculative appreciation: 'Give that child another five years . . . wow!'

'Lecher,' Jason rebuked, then grinned. 'All the same, I'm going to claim a dance with her – my wife permitting.'

'You may dance with Diane all evening,' Miranda returned sweetly, and in her heart wished it might be so. There was no danger from a dark-eyed, elfin child who was indeed near enough the threshold of womanhood to enchant quite a few male hearts that evening. During the dancing that followed Diane never lacked a partner and while the older women watched her sparkling triumph with indulgence Miranda heard one petulant young woman remark acidly that really it was ridiculous allowing children to stay on so late.

'Does she worry you, darling?' said an anonymous voice, and Sir Charles, who had claimed Miranda for that particular dance, also overheard. He chuckled gruffly as he swept her on to the floor. 'Afraid that niece of mine is going to cause havoc in a few years' time – she's a minx already. You know that she's just annexed your husband to get her a drink?'

She smiled. 'He was quite happy to be annexed, I think.'

Sir Charles nodded, then looked down quizzically into her face. 'But now, my dear, now that I have a chance to talk to you, how are you and Jason settling down together? – if it's not an impertinent question.'

She shook her head – Sir Charles was too courtly ever to be impertinent – and said quietly, 'Very well, thank you.'

'Good!' He lowered his voice confidingly. 'I'm glad that he finally decided to take the plunge. I'm a great believer in marriage. It stabilizes a man, especially a man in Jason's position. He needed someone like you, and my wife and I were beginning to despair of ever seeing him settle down.' Sir Charles paused, concentrating on guiding her through a reverse turn in his rather stiff, old-fashioned way before he added: 'Quite apart from hoping that when he did he would choose the right girl.'

She stayed silent, acknowledging the compliment with a smile. She was well aware of the fact that many firms vetted their employees' wives before considering them for promotion, and she suspected that this was done discreetly in some cases by Carona-Steele. But in Jason's case there was no one to say him nay, except Sir Charles, and she felt sure that even Sir Charles would hesitate to wield the seniority of age to interfere in Jason's personal life.

There was no sign of Jason and the youthful belle of the evening when the music ended and Sir Charles escorted Miranda back to the rim of the big room.

'It seems I can't return you to your partner,' he said an air of mock drama. 'Shall we join them, my dear?'

'Thank you – no.' She shook her head. 'I think I'll go and

cool off for a few minutes.'

She threaded her way slowly through the clusters of guests until she reached the wide windows at the end of the room. For a moment she stood, her eyes remote, then she unlatched the window and walked out on the terrace, drawing deep breaths of the refreshing night air.

Sir Charles's words had made a deep impression on her, and more than anything else she wanted to believe they were true: that she was the right girl.

If only she could believe that Jason did need her!

Through the open window the strains of music sounded again. She half turned to go indoors again, then changed her mind and drifted along the terrace. Several other guests had found the heat indoors a little overwhelming and were leaning on the terrace rail, sipping drinks, or strolling in the garden.

If only Jason had mentioned Lissa! Why did he avoid any reference to the girl he had wanted to marry? Why had he betrayed anger that day weeks ago when she had told him of Lissa's visit? And Lissa had made no further contact with her ... *because Jason had warned her not to make social contact with his wife*? suggested the cruel voice of intuition. No! Inwardly she recoiled from the implication of that answer.

Almost angry, this time with herself. Miranda halted on the shadowy path along which her steps had led her automatically. She must stop worrying and have more trust in the enigmatic man to whom she had entrusted her happiness and her future. And she had better get back in case he was wondering where she had got to. He might need rescuing from Diane! Stifling a giggle which held just a slight trace of hysteria, she began quickly to retrace her steps.

She reached the end of the tall hedge, and heard Lissa's voice. Another second of time and Miranda would have walked into her, but in that second she saw that Lissa was not alone.

Miranda froze, and her heart turned to ice. She did not need to see the face, just the tall dark male outline that belonged only to one man in the world.

Suddenly the sounds of revelry in the background stilled in Miranda's ears and everything receded. There was only the dark outline of Jason's head and the soft voice saying:

'But why won't you tell me, Jason?'

'Because I don't choose to, my sweet.'

'But I've got to know,' the soft voice persisted. 'I know she's in love with you – one has only to look at her to know it – but are you madly in love with your little wife, darling?'

There was the briefest of hesitations, then: 'I don't think that need concern us . . .'

There was a definite emphasis on the word 'us' that turned the ice into daggers of pain. Miranda clutched at her throat. She wanted to tear herself away before she saw the kiss that would spell the ruin of her happiness, and at the same time she wanted to attack this elusive enemy who had shadowed her marriage ever since its eve. But fear, and hunger for the truth, no matter how destructive, kept her a silent prisoner under the dark, whispering trees.

She gave a soft, shuddering sigh, and that sigh was echoed by the girl only a metre or so away.

'No, Jason. As ever, you're almost too wise. Actually, I don't think I want to know. Because whatever happens, she's your wife. But at least it's put an end to James' suspicions.'

'Was he suspicious?' There was a sharper note in Jason's voice. Was it fear?

'I think so. But as soon as he heard the news he was delighted. In fact, I'd say it was a stroke of genius. I mean,' Lissa's hands fluttered like pale moths in the darkness, 'we couldn't have thought of a better smokescreen. Did I tell you it was his idea to have you both down for a week-end? Even I wouldn't have gone as far as that. So you'll have to – Oh, Jason, quickly!' – the pale moths fluttered to draw down his head – 'I think someone's coming and I'm aching for—'

Miranda's limbs came back to trembling life.

White-faced, sick to her heart, she turned away and fled towards the glow of light from the terrace. The other light foot-steps danced nearer and she came face to face with Diana.

'Oh, there you are!' the child laughed. 'I've been looking for you – Aunt Eleanor sent me to round up the people outside to tell them the cabaret is starting – that is if you want to see it. But you won't want to miss Rudi Ricardo. He's absolutely super-de-fabulous! But where's—?'

'He isn't here. He – he's with your uncle.' Still reeling, Miranda hardly knew what she was saying as she seized Diane's arm.

'But he wasn't, not a minute ago. Uncle Ch—'

'It – it doesn't matter.' Almost fiercely she was hustling Diane back towards the house. There was only one thought in

157

her mind now. Whatever happened, Diane must not see. No one must see ...

But she reckoned without Diane's youthful perception, and the unguarded question as Diane glimpsed her distraught expression in the brilliant light streaming from the window.

'What's the matter?' Diane stopped short. 'Are you feeling ill?'

'No, I'm all right.' Beyond someone's shoulder she saw Lissa approaching the steps leading up to the terrace. For an instant Miranda closed her eyes. Then she turned her head and forced her stiff lips to stretch into a travesty of a smile. 'No, Diane, I'm perfectly all right ...

Her head held high, she walked alone into the assembly of guests. This then, was heartbreak ...

CHAPTER TWELVE

AFTERWARDS, she did not know how she got through the rest of that evening.

The shock of betrayal surged in her like a tempest, threatening to burst out of control every instant. Only an innate strength of character, and because the very special nature of the occasion almost demanded it, made her feel bound to try to pretend that nothing had happened.

But try as she might, she could not bear to face the other girl, let alone assume the bright social face of politeness, and when Jason came to her side she stiffened.

'Like a drink?'

Was it imagination, or was his voice forced, his manner wary?

Her own voice stuck in her throat and she dared not look at him. She shook her head and kept it averted. Fortunately the Latin-American singer had taken up his hand mike and was standing by the piano, making a special greeting to Sir Charles and Lady Hubard and announcing the song he would sing first to mark the occasion.

For a while she did not have to speak to or look at Jason. She saw Diane at the other side of the room, as near to the piano as she could edge, her small upturned face enrapt as she stared at her current idol. Then Diane's face blurred, and the husky velvet voice of Rudi proved the open sesame that no human control could have resisted at that particular moment.

The tears spilled hot from her anguished eyes and her mouth worked convulsively. She turned blindly and slipped from the room. She went through the deserted hall, into the cloakroom. There, the locked door behind her, safe from curious eyes, she took great sobbing breaths while she fought for control. Very slowly control won and she opened tightly clenched hands, pressing them on the cold marble rim of the washbasin.

The wild thoughts of running away, of staying to confront Lissa, of pouring out hot accusations to Jason, gave way to the numbed calm of despair. In a strange way she was experiencing release, release from the suspicion and the doubts that had tormented her for so long. She wanted so desperately to believe in Jason that she had fought them, but instinct had been right all along. The old affair between Jason and Lissa had never ended, despite the fact that each had chosen to marry another.

A smokescreen, Lissa had said.

Miranda stared at her white, frightened face in the mirror. Perhaps Jason had had that in mind from the start. This was why Rena had tried to warn her, and she'd been too blind, too naïve, too possessed by Jason's spell to take heed.

But what was she going to do?

With trembling hands she got out her compact and tried to repair the ravages of emotion. Her efforts were not entirely successful, but suddenly she ceased to care about her personal appearance. Only one thing was of importance now.

When she returned to the hall Jason was standing at the foot of the stairs. He stubbed out his cigarette with jerky movements and spun to face her, and his expression seemed to betray everything she needed to confirm her fears: anxiety – and guilt.

'Where did you vanish to?'

'Really, Jason, what a question!' she exclaimed.

A dark flush suffused his cheeks, and his own mouth tightened. 'Make-up repairs, I suppose.'

'You suppose right.'

'But why do they take hours? – come on, it's nearly over. This is the last dance.'

She allowed him to walk her back into the big room, and draw her, taut and silent, into his arms for the last dance. An air of unreality descended on her, and she almost exclaimed her disillusion aloud when the musicians struck up their ironic choice of music, the Wedding Waltz.

Jason said something, and at her monosyllabic response he stopped abruptly.

'What's the matter?' he said quietly.

'Nothing.'

She did not look at him, and he began moving again. 'Got a headache, or something?'

She wanted to scream, *Or something just about wraps it all up!* Instead she stared unseeingly past his shoulder. 'I'm perfectly all right,' she gritted.

'You don't look it.'

'Thanks,' she said tersely.

'You know perfectly well I didn't mean it that way.'

'Then which way did you mean it?'

She felt the soft groan he gave under his breath and wished with all her heart that the music would end and they could end the charade their relationship had become. It seemed that he harboured the same sentiment, for he whispered almost inaudibly: 'Oh, God, this is interminable!'

When at last the final flourish of the drums ended he muttered, 'Come on, let's say our good nights and get out of here.'

When they had done so and reached the car Miranda was shivering with dread.

She huddled back in her seat while Jason extricated the car from the mix-up of all the other cars trying to leave at the same time. Somewhere two bumpers met with the sickening metallic crunch which accompanies such encounters, and Jason exclaimed impatiently: 'Wally, for a pound. He shouldn't drive in the state he's in, the fool.'

She made no response but a shiver, almost wishing she were as intoxicated as Wally Ambrose had appeared to be by the end of the evening. Jason noticed the shiver, and with a brusque movement reached over into the back and snatched the rug. He tossed it across her lap, leaving her to sort out the folds herself and shrink into its warmth while he manoeuvred the car past the interlocked pair and the arguing drivers. Suddenly the road was clear before the big car and Jason accelerated into the night. The silence began to press like a tangible thing, as though it were urging her to break it, but now she was alone with Jason the cold sickness was numbing the pit of her stomach and she did not know what to say. How did one begin to say the things that must end the mockery of a marriage charade?

He must have noticed the movement of her head. 'Not now – save it,' he said rather sharply.

'Is there anything to save?' she said bitterly.

'I could ask you that.'

The curt response stung her to anger. 'I saw you with Lissa,' she said baldly.

'I suspected that. It was the only thing I could think of that might have upset you back there.'

'Upset me? *Might* have *upset* me!' she cried incredulously. 'Is that all you can say?'

'No. I could say a great deal more,' he said coolly, 'but I'd prefer not to be driving a car when you lose control of your emotions.'

She clenched her hands so tightly the nails bit into the palms but she felt no pain. Every particle of sensation was concentrated in a surge of near hatred for a man who could express so callous a disregard for her feelings. 'You mean you have no intention of explaining – you never had,' she choked.

'There's very little to explain,' he said in the same, tight, emotionless tones. As though to underline this, almost as though to dismiss a tiresome subject, he came down hard on the throttle and the car leaped into speed, the needle hovering dangerously past the seventy mark.

'Am I not entitled even to that?'

There was no reply. The car hurtled on, through the tearing streaks of scarlet and white lights, towards the carpet of London's glow in the distance. She had never known Jason drive so viciously, and when at last he drew to a halt in the dark safe confines of Byrne Square she was trembling. Still in silence, he garaged the car and let them into the house. The weakness of reaction overcame her suddenly and she stood in the hall, her light wrap sliding from her shoulders.

Jason walked past her, into the lounge, and went to the cocktail cabinet. He poured two measures of whisky and held one out to her.

'No, thanks.' Listlessly she bent to pick up the wrap and dropped it over the hall chair. 'It would choke me.'

He shrugged, and drained his own glass. 'So you spied on me tonight.'

She jerked upright. 'How dare you! I don't spy!'

'No?' His brows went up. 'If you'd stayed and spied a little longer you might have realized that Lissa was making the running, not I.'

'Does it matter who was making the running?' Her voice went dull and her eyes shadowed with lifelessness. He had taken the offensive, the last reaction she had expected from him. He wasn't even going to deny it.

'On the contrary, it does.' He surveyed her with eyes in which more than a hint of anger lurked. 'You, listened, didn't you? And then Diane came barging along and you ran way. It's a pity you didn't listen a while longer. You would have heard me telling Lissa that the affair was over, for good.'

'So it was Lissa all along.' She turned away, the echoes of her own words throbbing like a death knell in her heart.

'*Was*,' he emphasized, his mouth compressing. 'I thought everyone in town knew.'

'Except me.'

'Listen, Miranda. I didn't ask for a blow-by-blow account of your past love affairs when I married, so why should I recount mine?' he demanded.

'I never had any, except ...' Her mouth quivered and she could not go on.

'I'm aware of that.' He paced back to the cabinet. 'It might have been different if I hadn't,' he added dryly. 'Experience and innocence never made a good equation.'

She shook her head, too spent to parry his cynical observations, and sank into a chair.

He stood with his back to her, pouring himself a second stiff measure, and said over his shoulder: 'However, as I know you won't be satisfied till you've the whole story in your possession, I'll tell you ...' The drink in his hand, he lounged negligently against the cabinet, a steely glint in his eyes.

'Yes, I had an affair with Lissa. It lasted nearly a year, and ended when she chose to marry James Lindsterne, for reasons which are irrelevant at this moment. I thought the affair was over, and I saw her on about three occasions, all strictly social, during the following months. As far as I was concerned, that was the end of our relationship. I'll admit I was bitter – she was the only woman who'd ever got under my skin to the extent that I was no longer in control of the affair – and I reacted predictably by seeking feminine consolation elsewhere. Not very wisely, either.

'Oh, yes,' a bitterness hardened his mouth as he swirled the spirit in his glass and stared at it for a moment before he drank, 'Lissa has a good deal to answer for in my personal life. Then she suddenly chose the most psychologically dangerous moment to come back into my life.' He looked up. 'Remember the night you camped in my office?'

She nodded, hoping against hope that he wasn't going to destroy any more of her illusions but knowing in her heart the vainness of that hope.

'When I left you that evening I'd just got back here when the phone rang. It was Lissa. She'd been to Rome to visit her sister Claire. Through a flight cancellation she got back – came back deliberately – a night earlier than planned. Her husband didn't know. So,' Jason set the glass down, 'she came straight here – and stayed the night.'

Miranda closed her eyes, an involuntary betrayal of distress.

His mouth twisted. 'Don't look like that – damn it all! I was in love with her. I hadn't *seen* her for months. Then she came here, out of the blue, and walked into my arms. I was feeling as wretched as hell that night – she couldn't have picked a more opportune moment. I'd had one flaming row with a two-timing little bitch – Catrina had a heart of stone and a brain like a bank computer,' he interjected disgustedly. 'Lissa just seemed like everything I'd ever wanted and lost suddenly coming back to me. Afterwards, I wondered if that night had been real. Then I wondered how I was going to forget her again, because I knew it had just been one of those mad, impulsive things that happen, and I knew that to pick up our affair again could only lead to trouble.' He paused.

'Then she rang me a few days later – with the soft enticement of a clandestine week-end. James was going to Scotland and she could meet me somewhere quiet in the country. I was tempted, and then suddenly I thought of James. He's a bit of an ass, but he's totally honest. I began to wonder if she'd have taken a lover had she married me. I felt sorry for him, and disgusted with myself and Lissa. The last thing I wanted was to cuckold an old friend. That was the moment when I began to master my desire for her.'

Miranda stood up, sick at heart, and a shiver ran through her shoulders. Against her will, she was forced to recognize the ring of truth in his statement. She believed he had genuinely intended to end the affair when Lissa married – for how could any self-respecting man bear to abase pride to the extent of allowing any woman who refused his proposal of marriage to continue to call the tune – but nothing could hide the other truth now: he still loved her . . .

She felt his eyes follow her movement, and giving a small, despairing shake of her head she moved towards the door. 'Miranda . . .' His voice halted her. 'I haven't finished.'

Her head drooped wearily. 'I don't want to hear any more.'

'Maybe not, but it's a bit late to change your mind.' The coldness returned to sharpen his tone. 'It occurred to me some time ago to wonder how many tales you'd heard about me.'

The involuntary murmur she made brought an exclamation of grim satisfaction to his lips. 'I thought so. It was inevitable in the circumstances. And it explains quite a few small dispositions about you which I've noticed since our marriage.'

She looked round. 'Such as?'

He shrugged. 'I'm beginning to know more about you than you know yourself, but I'd be surprised if that was the nature of your concern at this moment.' He came towards her. 'It's over, Miranda.'

'Is it?' she whispered.

He put his hands on her shoulders and deliberately turned her to face him. 'Tell me, can you produce one iota of valid proof that I've been unfaithful to you since our marriage? Or do you prefer to believe your own unfounded suspicions – and gutter tales – before my word? Lissa is past. And I have never been unfaithful to you.'

She wanted to be convinced, and she desperately wanted to believe that the shadow of Lissa would dim into the past, that the time would come when her memory ceased to exist for him. But she needed time to adjust, and tenderness to heal the hurt that was holding her very near the verge of tears. When he put his arms round her she stood passive, without desire, and was totally unprepared for the sudden upsurge in him of passion. His mouth came down hard, parting her lips and forcing her head back, and when the rough strength of his hand bruised the softness of her breast she experienced a wave of rejection. The face of Lissa swam before her eyes, here in this very room. *'The only woman who ever got under my skin . . .'*

'Don't touch me!' She flung away from him.

His face darkened. 'Why shouldn't I? You're my wife.'

'That's all you married me for, isn't it?'

'Is that what you think?'

She whirled to face him, her eyes brilliant with unshed tears. 'What else am I to think? You made it plain enough when you asked me to marry you. If I'd been willing to have the affair you wanted would you have married me?'

His mouth set grimly. 'A man doesn't marry only for sex, Miranda. I could have had a dozen girls.' He took an angry pace forward and his hands clenched. 'Tell me, just *what* do you expect from me? I've tried to meet your needs. Material, physical, and social. How much more do you want? To own me; body and soul?'

She recoiled. 'I don't want to own you at all, but neither will I share you.'

'You haven't been expected to share me – with another woman,' he retorted. 'That's what you mean, isn't it?'

She raised one hand, then let it fall despairingly. She shook her head, then looked at him, her eyes dull. 'Jason,' she said slowly, 'why did you marry me?'

He seemed startled, as though he had expected her to say something else. 'What makes you ask?'

She shrugged wearily. 'I've often wondered. Because I've always known that it wasn't because you were in love with me.'

He hesitated, and when he started to speak he did not look at her. 'I thought you'd already worked it out to your own satisfaction. Or perhaps dissatisfaction would be a more apt description. I've never attempted to analyse my reasons, but since you say so,' his mouth went down at the corners, 'yes, it's true in that respect. I knew I'd never get anywhere with you without marriage. So, on impulse, I married you. To be strictly honest, I suppose it was on the rebound – isn't that the classic way of describing it?'

The silence lengthened after his voice died away. He poured another slug of whisky, splashed soda into it, took a mouthful and abruptly set down the glass. He made a grimace of distaste and sighed. With even paces he crossed the room, and as he neared her she watched him with wary eyes.

He stopped, and his expression was hard. 'However, you've made your opinion of me perfectly plain tonight, so what else is there to say?'

The rift yawned wide, deep and cold. Across it she met the

grey ice of his mocking glance, and could find no answer to his question. Her head bowed, and a moment later the soft draught from the door stirred a fold of her dress. When she looked up the room was empty.

*　　*　　*

The next three days were the longest and unhappiest she had ever experienced.

Jason remained cold and remote. She saw him only at breakfast and late in the evenings when he returned, grim-faced and taciturn, and suddenly she was haunted by the fear that he didn't care if the rift remained permanently unbridged.

During the lonely dragging hours when sleep eluded her and she lay wondering if he too were lying wakeful in the next room the memory of the Saturday night stayed doggedly in her brain. Over and over again she relived those hours and their miserable climax, and each time she asked herself despairingly how much of the blame lay on her conscience.

Did she seem too possessive? Did she expect too much of a man's faith in this day and age? Did he love her in the only way he knew? '*I've tried to provide for your needs. Material, physical, and social . . .*' In this case, was she throwing away everything for the sake of a dream? Was her long cherished idea of love simply devotion to a myth? Did that kind of love ever exist, except in the imagination of poets and story-tellers?

By the third morning Miranda had gathered her courage together. They couldn't go on like this much longer. She rehearsed what she was going to say, schooled herself for a quiet practical attitude, and made sure she was first down to breakfast on the Wednesday morning. And then all her careful intentions fled.

In cold horror she saw him bring down a suitcase.

Her cheeks blanched as she saw him set it down beside the hall chair on which his executive case rested. If he noticed her fear-filled glance he gave no sign, and in silence he ate breakfast, unhurriedly, giving no indication if he noticed that she ate not a mouthful. At the toast stage he took up the *Telegraph* and there was not a tremor or an untoward rustle to betray any inward perturbation he might be feeling.

He was leaving her!

There couldn't be any other explanation. There had been no mention the previous week of any more business trips, and usually Jason had everything, all appointments and journeys, arranged well in advance.

For the first time in three days she forgot the ridiculous state of 'not speaking' in this fresh spate of horror.

'Where are you going?' she faltered.

The paper went down a few inches. He looked at her over the top. 'I beg your pardon . . .?' he said coldly.

Her lips were dry. 'I – I asked: where are you going?'

'Bonn.'

The paper went up again, but in the painful surge of relief she scarcely noticed. 'Oh, of course! You – you never got there, after Rome. You were . . .' Her voice trailed off. She wanted to ask how long he would be away, but obviously the moment was not yet propitious for asking questions. She reached for the coffee-pot and with a quivering hand poured out a cup for herself. As she took the first mouthful he stood up.

He said, 'I'll be back on Saturday. We'll talk then – if you've come to your senses.'

The tentative words to wish him a safe trip died on her lips, and before she could form protest or denial he had gone, leaving her to make what she could of his parting words.

Long before the day was over she was convinced that there was only one thing he wanted to talk about; the ending of their marriage.

Suddenly she couldn't bear to stay in the house a moment longer. Without any conscious idea of where she would go, she shouldered into the first jacket that came to hand, grabbed her handbag, and hurried out. She wandered round the shops, finding no joy or temptation in the cosmetic departments she normally loved, and felt as though some invisible wall isolated her from the throng of shoppers sauntering past the fashion displays. It was not until she went into her purse for her fare home that she missed her compact, and immediately she felt panic: had she lost it?

A sense of tragedy swept over her and she could scarcely suppress the need to weep. It was not only the material value of the compact – like all Jason's gifts it had been expensive – but the fact that it *was* one of his gifts that mattered. She thought of getting out at the next stop and rushing back to the places she had visited that afternoon, only to realize that by then they would be closed. And then she remembered: it was still in her evening purse. She had never taken it out since the previous

Saturday. But when she got home, running upstairs in a fever of impatience to reassure herself, she discovered that the compact was not in the white and silver brocade purse.

She sank down on the edge of the bed, trying to remember when last she had used the compact, and the unhappy memory surfaced: she had used it when she ruined her make-up and left it there.

There was no reply at the Hubard home when she went to telephone, and it was not until the following morning she succeeded in making conact. Then Lady Hubard herself answered the phone.

She was instantly concerned. 'But of course I'll inquire, my dear. How distressing for you. To tell you the truth, there were several things left – two scarves that I know of, and an earring, and someone left a bottle of brilliant pink pills! Now just wait a moment. I'll ask Marie.'

There was the hollow sound of the receiver being laid on its side, and then the sounds of voices in the distance. Then Lady Hubard came back.

'Yes, my dear, there *is* a compact. Quite small. A silver one with a rather beautiful inset of butterflies – are they lapis-lazuli? I'm not—'

'Yes, that's the one,' Miranda said thankfully. 'I thought I'd lost it.'

'No, it's quite safe,' Lady Hubard soothed. 'Now, shall I send it to you? Or ask Charles to give it to Jason ...' She checked with a soft exclamation. 'Perhaps not – it's never wise to let our menfolk know when we've been just a trifle forgetful! But I've had a better idea – if you aren't too busy this week why not come over? We'd love to see you.'

As Miranda hesitated Lady Hubard suggested:

'Why not make it tomorrow, my dear? Come for the day and stay overnight. Then you can go with Charles to the airport on Saturday to meet Jason.' Carried away with her own enthusiasm, Lady Hubard made it impossible to refuse. Times were arranged, and she rang off, leaving Miranda looking forward with mixed feelings to this unexpected invitation. Although she liked the older woman very much the association with Jason was too close to face with equanimity at this time. Miranda had never been very good at dissembling, and the thought of having to speak of Jason as though nothing had happened filled her with foreboding. For if Lady Hubard should happen to be in one of her motherly moods the temptation to confide might overcome all other scruples.

When the taxi swept up the drive just after eleven the next morning Miranda found it difficult to credit that less than a week had elapsed since she drove with Jason up this same drive. It felt like aeons. She paid the driver and turned to see Lady Hubard hurrying across the lawn. Her hostess wore a voluminous green linen apron over her dove-grey summer dress, and a businesslike pair of gardening gloves which she pulled off before she took Miranda's hand and stooped to kiss her cheek.

'Welcome – and do forgive my earthy state!' She brushed traces of her recent activity from one knee and laughed. 'It isn't our week for the gardener until next week and Charles has been complaining of his back these past few days — I say it's a convenient excuse when there's weeding to be done! Now let us go in – I think I've earned my coffee this morning!'

One didn't have to worry about making conversation with Lady Hubard; she made it very easy just to smile and pick up the conventional cues. But Miranda knew instinctively that the two older people had taken a genuine liking for her, and this knowledge strengthened her resolution not to betray that anything was amiss. The last thing she wanted was to cause the embarrassment of alienation in a rather difficult situation. However, as the day passed, it became easier, and suddenly she was tremulously glad not to be spending another lonely, miserable day at Byrne Square.

After coffee she helped her hostess finish weeding the big circular rose bed outside the morning room window, and at lunch time Sir Charles arrived home. There was only one awkward moment, when he teased her about missing her husband, and then the subject of conversation turned to the wedding celebration, and then to Diane.

It wasn't until breakfast the following morning that Sir Charles said ruminatively: 'Did he say what time he'd touch down?'

Miranda shook her head. 'No, just that he would be back on Saturday,' she said carefully.

Her host's eyes widened. 'Well, that's useful. How typical of Jason! If he doesn't tell his wife who is he going to tell?'

Fortunately Lady Hubard instantly thought of a perfectly convincing explanation, and saved Miranda the awkwardness of responding.

'He probably didn't know until the last moment,' Lady Hubard said calmly, 'and he probably telephoned Miranda last night, not knowing she is here. It's quite simple.'

Sir Charles nodded. 'Didn't think of that.'

'You wouldn't,' said his wife sweetly. 'I sometimes wonder how men run businesses and countries at all. It isn't surprising that the world's in its present state of chaos.'

'Meaning the ladies might have done better?' he teased.

'No might about it,' she retorted. 'We would.'

His eyes twinkled. 'Now, now! I think you're a little too mature for Women's Lib, my dear.'

'Nonsense.' She turned a mock frown on her husband, then looked at Miranda. 'Would you like to telephone home and ask Libby if he rang last night?'

'Yes,' put in Sir Charles. 'We don't want to miss his flight.'

Miranda swallowed. 'It's very kind of you to offer to drive me to meet him, Sir Charles, but I don't think Jason will have rung – he doesn't like being met or seen off at airports, and so I . . .' She forced a smile and gave a tiny shrug.

'And so you respect his wishes instead of making an issue out of a small male foible; very wise of you, my dear,' Lady Hubard concluded for her. She raised fine brows at her husband. 'See how we defer to our lords and masters?'

For once Sir Charles failed to follow through the badinage which seemed to flow good-humouredly between them most of the time. 'Doesn't like being met . . .? I never heard such nonsense. That boy is becoming a shade too arrogant for his own good. Well,' he stood up and cleared his throat a trifle pompously, 'I'm afraid I'm going to risk displeasing him – there is a certain matter I must inquire about which I'd rather not have to wait until Monday to confirm.'

Still 'hrumphing', he went from the room, and his wife smiled secretively at Miranda.

Had she felt happier Miranda could have smiled at the chairman of Carona-Steele's reference to his managing director. At thirty-seven, Jason was scarcely her idea of a boy! Although she could understand that in Sir Charles' venerable eyes he might still appear that. A few minutes later Sir Charles returned.

'No news at your place,' he said, nodding to Miranda, 'so I got on to Miss Mayo. Wakened her up, I'm afraid. Told her to get on to the airport people and check the passenger lists out of

170

Bonn this morning. Should be hearing from her within half an hour at the most.'

There was always a way of finding out, Miranda reflected while Sir Charles waited impatiently, provided you had the power of a massive business concern at your back. The call came through very soon, and the infallible Miss Mayo had used her initiative, as Sir Charles termed it approvingly. The Bonn departure lists had not included the name of Jason Steele – but the Frankfurt list had, and the flight was due in at noon.

Nearly three hours to go. Then the reckoning that might begin the ending of her brief marriage. Tension laid its grip on Miranda during that lazy, sunfilled morning in the garden overlooking the river, making her increasingly oblivious to all but her own thoughts. He had said: *We'll talk when I get back.* Almost as though his decision was already made. Had their marriage run the time which the affair would have endured, had she thrown aside all scruples and surrendered? Would he have begun to weary of her by now, begun the gradual easing out of the relationship? Did he bitterly regret his own surrender – of his freedom?

Imprisoned in her thoughts, she scarcely heard Sir Charles' muttered protest as he got stiffly out of his deckchair and went to answer some summons of Marie. Lady Hubard was lying back, her eyes closed, her features placid in repose, and a bee droned softly somewhere near Miranda's head. The slam of a door within the house sounded abnormally loud in that drowsy, peaceful summer morn, and Lady Hubard's eyes fluttered open momentarily. Then steps pounded heavily across the terrace and Sir Charles gasped:

'The plane . . . that was the airport . . .'

Lady Hubard started upright. 'Charles! What is it?'

He stood there, breathless, his cheeks ashen.

'The plane! There's a bomb on it!'

CHAPTER THIRTEEN

It was a nightmare, of course.

Miranda gripped the wood frame of the deck-chair sides until her hands hurt. She had to wake up, escape the terrifying comprehension that threatened to explode sanity. She closed her eyes, then stared up at Sir Charles, willing reality to return and that ashen mask of horror dissolve into the familiar genial features she knew.

'They had two warnings. One at Frankfurt just after the plane took off; and one here. They—'

His face wavered and blurred. *A bomb!* On the plane! On the plane Jason . . .

She struggled to her feet like a swimmer fighting to surface. Her limbs felt like water and shock gripped her throat. Lady Hubard looked as though she were frozen to stone, horror and disbelief staring from her incredulous eyes.

She gasped: 'Charles! *What did you say?* Did you say a—?'

'They're diverting the plane to sea. A full-scale emergency. But the Frankfurt report said the detonating device is linked to the landing gear.' He punched one clenched fist into the other palm. 'Of all the sheer satanic genius! Unless they can locate it in time . . .'

Suddenly he sagged, shrunken and aged, and Lady Hubard recoiled. 'But how will they land if—?'

There was no reply. Abruptly she jumped up. 'It can't be true! It's a hoax. Some madman's perverted sense of humour. They're always ringing airlines to say there's a bomb on a plane, and time after time it proves to be another practical joker.'

She saw Miranda's groping hands and rushed forward to support her, putting a strong arm round her shoulders. 'Charles, get some brandy! I think she's going to faint. Oh, if I could get my hands on the— Hurry, Charles!'

'I'm not. I—' Miranda fought for control and lurched forward. 'I've got to get there. How do I get there? Her voice rose. 'I've got to get to Jason!'

'Steady.' The firm arm round her shoulders tightened. 'I'm sure it's going to turn out a false alarm, but fright won't help Jason, my dear.' She guided her across the lawn and through the open garden door. 'Now sit down until it passes.'

Sir Charles came back almost immediately, followed by a distraught-looking Marie. He passed the glass to his wife, who held it to Miranda's white lips. 'Now sip that, my dear, then we must try and find out what's happening.'

'Shall I fetch the little wireless from the kitchen?' asked Marie.

'No – they haven't released it yet to the press,' Sir Charles said, shaking his head. 'I think we'd better go to the airport.'

But Marie had gone, to return with the small black transistor set. As Sir Charles had said, there was no report, and impatiently he turned the volume control to mute the strident music.

Lady Hubard watched Miranda anxiously, sighing as a tinge of colour began to return to the white cheeks. 'I thought they had detectors to trace explosives now, since the wave of hijackings started.'

'This isn't a hijacking – it's a reprisal. And it's a long-range flight – Frankfurt's a major stopping place on the long distance international air routes.' Sir Charles paced backwards and forwards across the room as he spoke. He halted. 'Let's get over to the airport and see—'

'Ssh!' Lady Hubard's keen ears had caught the fade-out of music. She rushed to the radio and turned up the volume. The crisp voice flowed into the room:

'—news flash! A report has just come in concerning a bomb threat to a jet airliner at present on its way from Frankfurt to Heathrow. Two anonymous phone calls have been received during the past hour, one by German police, the other by New Scotland Yard, stating that a bomb has been placed aboard the aircraft. The plane, a Boeing 707, is on a routine flight from the Far East. There are 173 passengers and crew aboard including four children. No details have yet been issued, but the authorities are not treating it as a hoax . . .'

The voice stopped. There was a pause, then the music came back. Miranda felt sick. Fear closed like a wall around her and turned her hands to ice as she got into the car. What was happening up there? Did they know? Did Jason know? What were they doing to stop it? Before—? She shut her eyes against the dreadful thought and saw his image on her mind screen. Impossible to believe she might never see him again, never hear his voice, feel the touch of his hand . . . She was too shocked and terrified to weep, and in those moments she experienced so great a surge of love that all bitterness was forgotten. If by some miracle she were invested with supreme power she would have given anything to have him safe; and she would have given him Lissa if by doing so it brought him his heart's desire.

A second report came over the car radio, but it differed little from the first, except by adding the item of information

Sir Charles had already received. The news-reader's voice concluded: *'It is now known that the plane was delayed at Frankfurt earlier this morning while a minor technical irregularity was adjusted. Experts are discounting the terrorists' claim to have linked the explosive device to the aircraft's landing gear, but it is believed that the explosive has been smuggled aboard and concealed in some place innaccessible while the plane is aloft. Contact is being maintained from the control room of the south-eastern coastal airfield where officials, including a military explosives expert, are directing the search now taking place aboard the threatened aircraft.'*

A sigh escaped Lady Hubard, but she stayed silent. The same fear gripped her as gripped Miranda. If they had discounted the possibility of the landing gear triggering off the bomb, why then did they keep the plane in the air, above the sea, instead of bringing it down in some isolated airfield where more expert hands could seek the deadly seed it carried?

Unwittingly Sir Charles supplied one answer they were both too distraught to think of when he said suddenly: 'That's the trouble with the big jets – takes such a vast runway to bring them down.'

Lady Hubard sighed again and held Miranda's icy hands more tightly, trying to instil a measure of comfort and her own indomitable strength. And perhaps it was an obscure blessing that kept one other vital factor from entering their minds, thus postponing the impact of its own particular fear for a while.

But it could not be escaped much longer, once they reached the airport and the tense air of drama generated there. Checkpoints had been set up at access roads, where police turned back the invasion of would-be sightseers and the sensation-seekers. Sir Charles produced proof of identity and the police officer's expression softened momentarily as he glanced into the back of the car and saw Miranda's distraught young face.

They passed on, through the converging crowd of pressmen, photographers, TV cameramen, worried-looking officials and the frightened kinfolk of the passengers aboard the plane. Officials were evasive. No one wanted to commit himself, no one dared raise false hopes, no one seemed to have any definite information. In a private lounge a monitor screen had been hastily fitted, and there they were escorted, to wait and watch and pray while the frightening drama was played out in some anonymous sky, far above the sea.

Someone brought trays of tea, cups that were taken grate-
fully, sipped, then left to cool unheeded as the screen flickered
and the reports began again, each one adding so little to its
predecessor. For the first time four names were mentioned
from the passenger list: of a famous sportsman, of a diplomat,
of a Major Mark Shumann who was returning from the prov-
ince of Rhukal with his wife and baby, and Jason Steele.

A tremor went through Miranda and she sat forward, waiting, but there was no further information, and at last she slumped back despairingly.

'Why don't they tell us what they're doing?' someone
groaned.

There was a silence among the roomful of strangers drawn
together by the common bond of fear and suspense. Then Sir
Charles shook his head. 'They dare not release any details for
security reasons.'

Heads nodded, dully accepting his reason, and time dragged
by on leaden minutes. Noon approached, the hour which should
have seen the safe descent of the great plane and the reunion
with loved ones. It was then the other fear began: fuel and the
time factor.

How long could the plane stay up before its fuel reserves
were exhausted?

The nation sat by television or radio, its heart and prayers
going out to those trapped in this grim race with fate.

Numbness was pervading Miranda. She had almost reached
the stage where she dreaded the voice from the screen. It
brought nothing new, only the same facts they all knew by heart
now, and the emergency plans to divert all incoming air traffic
into the stacks when the plane was brought in. When . . .

Sir Charles got up for the ninth time and paced across the
room. He opened his lips to speak, and the voice came from the
screen. A gasp came from a score of throats and Miranda scarcely dared believe her ears, dared not believe it was true.

The bomb had been found.

A gabble of voices broke out. Everybody started to exclaim
at once, then someone cried 'Quiet!' and instantly hush came.
Every eye concentrated on the screen, nerves stretched to snapping point, waiting, and then the face of the newscaster flashed
back. He held notes, and now he was making little attempt to
sustain his former calm impartiality.

'*And now at last,*' he said quickly, '*time is not running out so fast for those one hundred and seventy-three men, women and children aboard the Boeing 707 which has been circling the air above the Channel since ten-forty a.m. this morning while the search was made by passengers and crew for an explosive device reported to be concealed on board. That device has been found! And now the two military experts in bomb disposal who have been standing by since the alarm was first raised and in constant contact with the aircraft are deciding on the next course of action. Very soon now we hope to bring you news everyone is praying for – that the danger will be overcome and the plane safely landed.'*

For a long while there was only the silence that followed the long, heartfelt sighs that came in unison from so many lips. Then a woman began to weep softly.

Miranda whispered: 'What will they do?'

Sir Charles looked down at her. 'Try to identify the type of device first – there are so many.'

'And the rough home-made variety are just as dangerous as the professional job,' put in a thin-featured, elderly man in a grey suit. 'Worse, sometimes, because they're less predictable.'

This information caused a visible tremor of fresh panic among some of the older people present, and a young girl hid her face in her hands.

Sir Charles cast an angry glance at the elderly man. 'Too much surmise is out of place at the present,' he said rather curtly. 'At least they now know what they've to deal with. Having been reasonably controlled for so long I suggest we try to remain patient a little while longer and try not to distress the women any more than they are already.' He bent down to his wife and Miranda. 'Be brave, my dears. I'm going to see if I can obtain any more information.'

He seemed to be gone a long time, until Miranda looked at her watch and discovered that only four minutes had elapsed since he left the lounge. Someone produced a packet of sweets and passed them round, and there was an almost feverish quality in the way they were unwrapped and slowly eaten. The screen remained blank, no one seemed inclined to talk, and each time anyone moved the gaze of everyone instantly swivelled in that direction.

Miranda looked at her watch again. Nine minutes. Where was Sir Charles? Why didn't he come back? Suddenly she needed his gruff strength.

'Look,' said someone. 'They've lost contact! What does that mean?'

A printed flash had appeared on the screen. *We regret we have temporarily lost contact with South-Eastern Coastal Air Control. We hope to bring you a further bulletin very soon.*

Lady Hubard said calmly: 'They've lost contact with Air Control. It doesn't mean that Air Control has lost contact with the plane.'

She stood up and went to the door, to look anxiously along the corridor. Miranda followed, to stand unsteadily in the doorway on limbs that ached with tension.

She constantly looked back towards the monitor screen. Lady Hubbard said, 'Where has he gone? – Tell me if I miss anything . . .'

Miranda stepped forward, not wanting to be left alone, then she saw Sir Charles coming back. He hurried towards them, looking flustered with excitement, and he was smiling. He opened his arms to his wife and Miranda, seizing their shoulders.

'It's going to be all right! It's coming in now!'

*   *   *

They rushed to watch, tensed to breaking point, silent, still afraid to believe that the nightmare could be over.

An electric hush descended on the airport. The skies were clear, and Miranda tried not to look at the ominous line-up of emergency service vehicles that had moved into position. She strained eyes and ears for the first sign and sound of the distant speck, and then someone cried: *'There it is!'* and a pent-up sigh ran through the spectators. The distant mote glinted, grew larger with incredible speed, and Miranda whispered a fervent prayer.

Never had the roar of the jets sounded so sweet and triumphant as the Boeing came down out of an innocent blue sky. Lower and lower it swooped, the massive landing wheels dropping smoothly like the outstretched claws of a great bird skimming down to earth. One second they were poised above the runway, then they touched down so smoothly the moment of impact was indiscernible. On the wings of its own impetus the plane rushed down the runway, slowing, checking, gliding the final few yards to quiver into a silent standstill, to Miranda, the most beautiful, majestic sight she had ever seen.

Suddenly there was pandemonium. Everyone wanted to reach it, everyone was shouting, and police and officials were repeating orders and instructions. And then the first of the passengers began to disembark.

A young woman emerged first, a stewardess and a tall, fair man supporting her. She looked white and shaken, but she stopped for a moment and looked round desperately until she saw the second stewardess who was following. The second stewardess was carrying a baby, and the young woman almost snatched the child from the girl, holding it tightly in her arms as she stumbled across to a waiting ambulance.

'Shock, I expect, poor child,' said Lady Hubard. 'What a dreadful experience for a young mother.'

Miranda scarcely heard her. She was watching the stream of passengers, waiting for the first glimpse of the tall dark familiar figure, and she did not register the fact that the stream of people from the Boeing were not approaching the usual clearance point but were being directed to another part of the passenger terminal cordoned off by security staff.

In panic she turned to Sir Charles. 'What's happening? Why aren't they . . .?'

'There's Jason!'

She spun round as Lady Hubard gripped her arm, and her eyes blurred with the tears of thankfulness. She blinked hard and willed him to see her, but he moved at that moment, alongside the fair man and another man in uniform. Jason appeared to be arguing, and her heart leapt with hope as he gestured, then he shrugged and turned away.

'I'm afraid you're going to have to be patient for a little while longer,' Sir Charles told her ruefully. 'We still don't know exactly what went on up there, and there's bound to be an inquiry. They'll want statements from everyone before they let them disperse.' He paused, cocking his head, 'And unless I'm mistaken the military have arrived.'

Sir Charles was proved right in each of these surmises. And when at last the moment of meeting came Miranda had reached the point of anti-climax. Lost were the moments when relief and emotion would have carried her passionately into his arms, unheeding of whether he wanted her there or not. Now she remembered that nothing had changed and was further inhibited by the presence of Sir Charles and his wife, and the many curious eyes still watchful everywhere.

She said, 'Jason . . .' unsteadily, taking a step towards him and waiting for him to respond.

He looked down at her, his eyes shadowed with strain. A strange, twisted little smile touched his mouth. 'Haven't you had enough of airports . . .?' He put his free hand on her shoulder and brushed his mouth over her cheek. 'Come on, let's go.'

'You're coming back with us.' Sir Charles was taking charge again. 'Your wife's been with us since yesterday morning, so I think you should spend the rest of the week-end with us while you recover from this nerve-racking experience.'

The brusque little salute on her cheek was all he could spare, she thought miserably, and saw his mouth tighten as Sir Charles spoke. She wondered if he were angry at the unexpected arrangement, for which she was indirectly responsible. Perhaps he had made other plans for the week-end, which he would have to cancel or risk offending the chairman.

But Jason made no protest. He voiced a polite 'thank you', and lapsed into silence when they got into the car. It was Lady Hubard whose patience gave out first.

'Well, Jason,' she exclaimed, 'please don't keep us in suspense any longer. Tell us what *happened*!'

'Who was responsible?' asked Sir Charles.

'Terrorists, as usual. But it was more in the nature of a personal reprisal,' said Jason grimly. 'How much information did they give out?'

'Practically none. Just the baldest facts,' said Lady Hubard.

'It's pretty certain that Major Shumann was the main objective, with the sheer horror that would have resulted, had the attack been successful, aimed on a broader scale at Britain in general. You may remember we signed a new lease three years ago for use of sea and air bases in Rhukal. Unfortunately, the subversive element on the island became so dangerous we were forced to take strong action. Major Shumann was sent out in charge of security, and – although this was never divulged – given a free hand to take whatever steps he thought necessary to deal with it. How successful he was can be judged by the peaceful atmosphere now happily present on the island. However,' Jason sighed, 'our enemies haven't forgotten. He has received threats of vengeance on three occasions, the last being in the shape of one those infernal letter bombs addressed to his wife, which luckily was spotted and dealt with before it ever reached her. When he—'

'Was that the big fair-headed fellow?' Sir Charles interrupted. 'I vaguely thought I recognized him.'

'Yes, he—'

'Charles, you're speeding!' Lady Hubard cut in. 'Sorry to interrupt, but there's a police car coming up in the inside lane and we've had quite enough excitement without being pinched for speeding.'

Sir Charles groaned under his breath and reluctantly dropped his speed to within the permitted seventy limit.

'I'm beginning to feel the urgent need of a stiff drink, and I'm sure Jason is.'

'Well, we won't be very long now.' Lady Hubard turned from her anxious survey of the patrol car behind them and flashed a placatory smile at Jason. 'Do forgive me – you were saying . . .?'

'He's just finished his term on Rhukal,' Jason went on, 'and was on his way home with his family. We were worried about his wife – she was suffering badly from shock.'

'Was that the young woman they took to hospital?'

'Yes, actually she wanted to go home, but it would have been difficult to keep the press away once the story broke, so it was decided to whip her away to a secret destination for twenty-four hours until she'd had a chance to get over her shock. When we—'

'But what were your reactions when you were told? Did they inform the passengers?' Sir Charles demanded anxiously.

'We'd just taken off from Frankfurt,' Jason said patiently. 'At first it was announced there was a technical fault – you know, the usual soothing soap – and there was nothing to be alarmed about, and that we were turning back. Everyone got back into their harness again and then the second announcement came over, that we were diverting but not to worry,' he added cynically. 'After a while, when no further gen was forthcoming and the stewardesses couldn't say what was happening we began to get a bit restive, Major Shumann in particular. Of course they had to tell us eventually because we had to search the bloody plane and everyone in it.' His mouth set grimly. 'And if you've never tried to sieve a Boeing in mid-air you haven't the faintest idea what the job entails. Anyway, about four of us, under the command of Major Shumann who seemed to take charge automatically, and the flight engineer, organized the search and decided not to tell the more nervous passengers exactly what we were looking for. We made up a story about smuggled arms and a threat of a hijacking which they accepted without question, and this made everyone doubly willing to submit to the search. After the first effort was unsuccessful we began to worry about the landing gear threat. But the flight engineer swore it was impossible. He'd personally supervised the minor repair that delayed us at Frankfurt and he said he'd stake his life that nothing had been interfered with, and obviously the gear was okay when the plane landed there.'

He paused. 'It was Mrs. Shumann who found it.'

Miranda held her breath.

'Where?' breathed Lady Hubard.

'Concealed in the baby's carrycot. It was the one piece of baggage we passed over.'

'Oh, my God!' Automatically Sir Charles had brought the car to a halt. 'How in the name of heaven did it get in there?'

Almost unseeingly they got out of the car and went into the house, where Sir Charles poured drinks for them all while Jason continued his account.

'We're not sure yet. But it must have been done by someone in close collusion with one of the staff employed by Major Shumann at his house in Rhukal, possibly even the maid who had helped Mrs. Shumann care for the child. Certainly someone they trusted.'

Lady Hubard's face was white with horror as the full implication of what had happened became obvious. Miranda's own emotional stress dimmed for a time as she imagined the shock and anguish suffered by the young mother. Her baby . . . how she must feel every time she remembered what might have been . . .

She murmured raggedly: 'How dreadful,' and for a moment Jason's glance rested searchingly on her strained face.

'It was.' His tone was clipped. He got up and paced restlessly to the window, and now the strain of the nightmare recently undergone showed in his movements and the tense line of his jaw. He said slowly: 'Those two army boffins were superb, fantastic. They were so calm. They did it really, not us. When we found the thing there was only only seven minutes left. Seven minutes between us and . . .'

Miranda felt her blood go cold.

'They packed as much know-how into those seven minutes as

181

most of us would take weeks to absorb, and as lightly as though we were trying to mend a fuse. They described the thing as though it were in front of their eyes, not ours. And somehow we disarmed it. With a minute and fifteen seconds to spare.'

He stared unseeingly at the peaceful, sun-gilded lawn, and Sir Charles gasped:

'Who's "we"? You don't mean *you*?'

Jason's shoulders lifted slightly.

'I have a fair knowledge of electronics, of engineering, and I know a little about explosives. The flight engineer knew a great deal more, and Major Shumann has had a lot of experience of arms and explosives, practical as well as theoretical. We just did exactly as we were told and answered the questions we were asked. And then we could come home,' he added simply.

In the silence that followed no one moved. Then the shrilling of the phone exploded into the silence and Miranda jumped with sheer shock. They stared at the phone, until Sir Charles moved and almost ran to the desk. He turned.

'It's the press.' His hand closed over the mouthpiece. 'I think they know you're here.'

Jason took a deep breath. For a moment he seemed about to refuse. Then Sir Charles said: 'Might as well get it over with.'

Jason walked to the phone without glancing to left or right of him. Sir Charles looked at his watch, and his wife noticed the gesture. She put her hand to her throat and gave a heartfelt sigh, her mouth curving in a ghost of a whimsical smile.

She got up and moved softly across the room, pausing to whisper to Miranda: 'I must go and see what happened to lunch – I've just realized we haven't had it! No,' she laid a light hand on the girl's shoulder, 'you stay there, my dear. This must have been a terrible fright for you.'

She went from the room, and after a glance at Jason Sir Charles followed, closing the door quietly.

Jason was sitting on the corner of the desk now, his back to Miranda, and his voice had regained its crisp decisiveness as he responded to the questions issuing metallically from the phone.

She stared at him, at the relaxed stance of him betrayed in one slowly swinging foot, in the long well-shaped fingers toying idly with a silver paper knife on the desk. He held it poised under one fingertip, its point in the centre of the blotter-pad, the silver blade rotating slowly under the motion of his hand.

Almost mesmerized by the movement, she sat stiffly upright in her chair, unbelieving that he could be so totally oblivious to her presence. An impulse sprang in her to run to him, wrest the instrument out of his hand and force him to notice her. She gripped the sides of her chair, and suddenly a sense of unreality seemed to push out the walls of the room. A hissing came in her ears and frightening weakness pervaded her limbs. Panic rose. She was going to faint ... With the fear came a total reversal of the emotion she had felt the previous instant. Pride came uppermost, bringing a fierce determination not to make an idiot of herself. The last thing she wanted was his pity.

She took deep breaths, praying that he wouldn't turn, that he would go on talking until she forced her trembling legs to support her as far as the door. In the cooler air of the big hall she paused, like a bird about to take flight, and stumbled towards the stairs. No one appeared, and she reached the first floor and her room as breathless as though she had run a race. She sank on the nearest chair, which was actually the dressing-table stool, and slumped forward on the cool glass surface.

She did not realize that reaction had set in and she was now experiencing the effects of the hours of strain. She knew only that the cold glass under her arms was a stay, while she waited for the sick leaden weight in the pit of her stomach to dissolve. In a few minutes it would pass, she would be all right, she would regain control ... this coldness would go ... her body wouldn't always persist in trembling like an aspen ...

When the door opened and closed with a snap she started round as though she'd been struck.

'What's the matter?' Jason asked.

'Nothing,' she whispered through stiff lips.

He looked at the wide brilliant eyes in the alabaster white face, and his mouth tightened. He walked across the room and deliberately took her unresisting hands.

'You're like ice. Why didn't you say so?' He took off his jacket and put it round her shoulders. 'I'll get you a hot drink.'

'No, I don't want anything.' She huddled into the jacket and avoided his gaze.

'I don't think you're in a fit state to know what you do want.'

There was exasperation in his tone. She shook her head numbly. 'I don't want any fuss,' she said desperately.

'Fuss! What the devil's the matter with you, Miranda?'

She recoiled, and a sobbing breath escaped her. 'Can't you leave me alone? I didn't ask you to—'

'Miranda!' His hands seized her by the shoulders, biting through the stuff of the jacket. He dragged her to her feet and held her facing him. 'Are you going to let the shadow of Lissa stay between us for ever? Can't you forget?'

His eyes glinted like steel crystal, and the strength of his fingers brought a bruising, physical pain. Suddenly she could take no more. Her voice choked on a cry and her mouth crumpled helplessly. Great tearing sobs shuddered through her, and with a soft groan Jason pulled her against this chest.

'Go on, go on,' he said against the top of her head, 'get it over with, then perhaps we can start and talk sense.'

He held her close, waiting for the storm of tears to spend themselves, until the moment she stirred and sniffed unhappily, and said weakly: 'I'm sorry . . . I – I didn't want to make a fool of myself.'

'Why foolish? And why sorry?' He pushed a clean handkerchief into her groping fingers. 'Now that you've got that out of your system you'll feel better, and perhaps you'll answer my question.'

'What question?' she mumbled into the handkerchief.

A sigh heaved his chest. 'This has certainly been a day . . . You know perfectly well which question, you idiot.'

'How can I?' She wouldn't look up. 'You love her.'

'Love her? Give me strength! I do not love her. I love *you*!'

There could be no mistake about his words. Jason's voice was of a particularly rich and resonant timbre. He never mumbled, nor was he given to mincing his words in moments of stress. Yet still she was not entirely convinced. She squashed the handkerchief into a tight ball and raised tear-stained eyes.

'You've never said so,' she quavered.

'Haven't I? Well, I'm saying it now.'

She looked up at his unsmiling mouth and with all her heart wanted to believe him. But conviction refused to come. She put one hand against his shoulder in a weary gesture of rejection and turned away.

'How do you expect me to believe that? You married me on the rebound. You admitted it yourself.'

She walked blindly to the window, fighting to keep from

further foolish tears, and after a hesitation he moved slowly to her side. He put one arm across her shoulders.

'That isn't entirely true, Miranda. We all say things that are not entirely true when we're angry, and I was very angry that night. Angry with you, because you wouldn't trust me. Angry with Lissa, because she wouldn't let the past go. And most of all I was angry with myself. But even then I still wasn't prepared to be honest about my own feelings.'

He paused, and his fingers tightened on her arm. 'I'll be honest. I never really believed in the kind of love I knew instinctively you were seeking. Any ideals I ever cherished were smashed at a very early age. I was hurt badly in my first love affair and I never forgot it, and the more experience I acquired the more convinced I became that your kind of love was like the crock at the end of the rainbow. Maybe I was unlucky with my women, but all the girls I met seemed the same. And if you'll try to be impartial you'll have to admit that a hell of a lot of girls are deliberately provocative. They want a man to desire them. They set out to provoke physical desire, and then scream disillusion when the man takes them at their own valuation and they find they've evoked only an illusion of love. And therein lies the heartbreak.' He took a deep breath. 'When I met Lissa I thought she was different, and once again I was wrong. And so, when I met you I knew you *were* different, but I wouldn't let myself believe that our marriage could eventually fulfil all those ideals I'd turned my back on, those same ideals you believed in so fiercely. I knew you were attracted to me, and I knew you'd never be unfaithful to me, but I wanted your trust as well.'

'Why didn't you say all this to me a long time ago?' she asked in a low voice.

'Because I was too proud. And I hadn't been forced to face eternity. In those seven minutes I learned more about life and myself than in the thirty-seven years I've existed.'

Her mouth quivered. 'I thought you didn't care. And when you scarcely spoke to me at the airport . . .' She bit on her lip to stop its trembling. 'You didn't even assume the mask of charm.'

'Mask of charm!' He jerked her towards him. 'Is that how you think of me?'

'I didn't know what to think of you at the finish.'

'How could I say these things at a time like that?' he

groaned. 'Under a thousand eyes . . .' He looked down into her woebegone face. 'I'm sorry, my darling, to be the cause of all this,' he touched the tear-stained cheeks and the wet lashes, 'I'd better do something about it . . .' Gently he kissed the flushed cheeks, the sad eyes, and then the soft mouth. 'I *do* love you, my darling. How can I convince you?'

'Oh, Jason . . .' Her arms went round his neck and she clung hard to him, letting the alchemy of love work its magic and its healing.

'Doesn't it all add up?' he asked, a few moments later. 'Remember our wedding night?'

She made a tiny movement against his shoulder.

'You were pretty miserable that night, and you blamed me, didn't you?'

She tensed, then shook her head. 'No – I blamed myself.'

'So you told me at the time, but you were still uncertain of me then,' he said softly. 'But surely by now you know my moods well enough to realize that when you evaded me that night you made me want to possess you so violently I was afraid of the outcome. I had to force myself to be patient. You see,' he ran disordering fingers through her hair, 'I knew from the start that under that cool, prim way of yours you possessed a deeply passionate generosity of loving – for the right man. But you were still a babe in the ways of passion, and any man with an iota of perception doesn't expect a babe to run before it walks. That's why I held back, very much against my more selfish desires.'

'Because you were so sure you were the right man?' With a joyous quickening of her heart she knew she could tease.

His mouth quirked. 'Do you think I'd have bothered if I hadn't loved you more deeply than I even realized myself? I should have thought that was one of your own idealistic conceptions of love – that in true love one considers the other's well-being before one's own desires?'

She sighed deeply. 'I wanted to believe that you would fall in love with me, but I was afraid to let myself, because of the way I felt about you, and because of that charm of yours – you just can't help being the most devastating man in the whole world. And,' she sighed again, 'you'd been so honest about the usual thing.'

'What usual thing?' He gave her a shake.

'Well, wanting to make love to me,' she said in a small voice.

'Oh, my darling little idiot!' He enfolded her closer. 'Whatever you have been taught to believe about men and their desires, there's one vital little aspect to which you seem blind. Tell me, could you allow *any* man to possess you?'

She looked at him in horror, her lips forming the shocked denial.

'Well, do you really believe it's impossible for a man to share a similar sentiment? Whatever you may have heard to the contrary most men are capable of feeling love in their hearts as well as their loins. And if you find that difficult to credit – heaven forbid! – can't you believe there's an exception to every rule? That exception being me?'

'Naturally!' She laughed shakily, but she was still too close to the memory of anguish to shed its effects. There was still something that remained to be said, and in the fullness of her love she had to make the admission he deserved. She held his dark gaze steadily.

'Jason, I'm sorry.'

'What for?'

'For not trusting you. For being too impatient to wait for our relationship to come to maturity. I've been as much to blame,' she said slowly. 'I didn't have enough trust. But oh!' her arms tightened convulsively round him, 'I went through agonies of suspicion and jealousy . . .' The memory of Rena Harvey, of Rome, a magazine in a dentist's waiting-room, flashed in rapid succession through her mind, but she bade them be silent. The barrier had gone down between herself and Jason; they could talk now, together, not at each other, and trust had flowered in its place. She murmured against his cheek: 'Love me and forgive me – because I love you so much, my darling.'

'Just go on loving me,' he whispered, and claimed her mouth with sudden fierceness of passion that took her breath away.

In the middle of the kiss a discreet tap came at the door.

Jason released her with a muttered: 'Damn!' and called, 'Come in.'

Lady Hubard put her head round the door. 'Doesn't *anyone* want any food? It's nearly four and we haven't yet had lunch!' She smiled. 'There's a buffet table in the dining-room, and three reporters in the lounge, Jason. Also, Miss Mayo just rang up to ask if you were here, if you were all right, and if she had to remain at the office.'

'Oh, lord!' Jason clapped a hand to his head. 'Poor May! I'd forgotten I'd told her to wait for me at the office and I'd call there on the way home from the airport.'

'And Charles is entertaining the B.B.C. in the library,' Lady Hubard added sweetly. 'Shall I say you'll be down in five minutes?'

'Can't we go out the back way?' he groaned.

'Afraid not,' she chuckled. 'Today you are notorious, my dear.' With a sympathetic smile for Miranda she withdrew and closed the door softly.

Jason closed his eyes despairingly. 'There'll be no escape for us today, I'm afraid. But I wonder ... shall we slip away to somewhere quiet tonight?'

She went back into his arms and framed his face with her hands. 'If you want to. I'm too happy to care where we are.'

It was true. All the assurance she had ever longed for was here now, in his arms drawing her close, in the love unhidden in his eyes, in the sweet joy of his mouth ... This was the end of the dream and the beginning of reality. This was her marriage.

16 GREAT RE-ISSUES

Here is a wonderful opportunity to read many of the Harlequin Romances you may have missed.

- [ ] 917 TIMBER MAN
  Joyce Dingwell
- [ ] 920 MAN AT MULERA
  Kathryn Blair
- [ ] 926 MOUNTAIN MAGIC
  Susan Barrie
- [ ] 944 WHISPER OF DOUBT
  Andrea Blake
- [ ] 973 TIME OF GRACE
  Sara Seale
- [ ] 976 FLAMINGOS ON THE LAKE
  Isobel Chace
- [ ] 980 A SONG BEGINS
  Mary Burchell
- [ ] 992 SNARE THE WILD HEART
  Elizabeth Hoy

- [ ] 996 PERCHANCE TO MARY
  Celine Conway
- [ ] 997 CASTLE THUNDERBIRD
  Susan Barrie
- [ ] 999 GREEN FINGERS FARM
  Joyce Dingwell
- [ ] 1014 HOUSE OF LORRAINE
  Rachel Lindsey
- [ ] 1027 THE LONELY SHORE
  Anne Weale
- [ ] 1223 THE GARDEN OF PERSEPHONE
  Nan Asquith
- [ ] 1245 THE BAY OF MOONLIGHT
  Rose Burghley
- [ ] 1319 BRITTLE BONDAGE
  Rosalind Brett

FREE!
Harlequin Romance Catalogue

Here is a wonderful opportunity to read many of the Harlequin Romances you may have missed.

The HARLEQUIN ROMANCE CATALOGUE lists hundreds of titles which possibly are no longer available at your local bookseller. To receive your copy, just fill out the coupon below, mail it to us, and we'll rush your catalogue to you!

Following this page you'll find a sampling of a few of the Harlequin Romances listed in the catalogue. Should you wish to order any of these immediately, kindly check the titles desired and mail with coupon.

To: **HARLEQUIN READER SERVICE, Dept. N 401**
   M.P.O. Box 707, Niagara Falls, N.Y. 14302
   Canadian address: Stratford, Ont., Canada

☐ Please send me the free Harlequin Romance Catalogue.

☐ Please send me the titles checked.

   I enclose $_____ (No C.O.D.'s), All books are 60c each. To help defray postage and handling cost, please add 25c.

Name _____

Address _____

City/Town _____

State/Prov. _____ Zip_____

Have You Missed Any of These
Harlequin Romances?

Have You Missed Any of These
Harlequin Romances?

All books are 60c. Please use the handy order coupon.

HH